WITHDRAWN

LIBRARY
College of St. Scholastica
Duluth, Minnesota 55811

# MOLECULAR COMPLEXES

*(Harris & Ewing, Washington DC)*
PROFESSOR R. S. MULLIKEN, NOBEL PRIZE WINNER

# Molecular Complexes

*by*

J. ROSE

M.Sc., Ph.D., F.R.I.C., F.I.L., M.B.I.M.

*Principal, College of Technology and Design,
Blackburn*

PERGAMON PRESS

OXFORD · LONDON · EDINBURGH · NEW YORK
TORONTO · SYDNEY · PARIS · BRAUNSCHWEIG

Pergamon Press Ltd., Headington Hill Hall, Oxford
4 & 5 Fitzroy Square, London W.1

Pergamon Press (Scotland) Ltd., 2 & 3 Teviot Place, Edinburgh 1

Pergamon Press Inc., 44–01 21st Street, Long Island City, New York 11101

Pergamon of Canada, Ltd., 6 Adelaide Street East, Toronto, Ontario

Pergamon Press (Aust.) Pty. Ltd., 20–22 Margaret Street, Sydney, N.S.W.

Pergamon Press S.A.R.L., 24 rue des Écoles, Paris 5ᵉ

Vieweg & Sohn GmbH, Burgplatz 1, Braunschweig

Copyright © 1967
J. Rose

QD
475
.R64
1967

First edition 1967

Library of Congress Catalog Card No. 67–22380

Filmset by Graphic Film Limited, Dublin, Ireland
and printed in Great Britain by
Compton Printing Ltd.,
London and Aylesbury
3238/67

To my brother Isaac

"Knowledge is of two kinds. We know
a subject ourselves, or we know where
we can find information upon it."

SAMUEL JOHNSON

LIBRARY
College of St. Scholastica
Duluth, Minnesota 55811

# CONTENTS

"The reward of a thing well done, is to have done it."

RALPH WALDO EMERSON

vii

# PREFACE

THIS work is concerned with a survey of the increasingly important and rapidly developing subject of molecular or addition complexes. The text consists of seven chapters; extensive bibliographies, with references covering a period of about 70 years up to 1966, are given at the end of each chapter.

The first chapter is concerned with the definition of the class of complexes considered and with the general reviews relating to molecular complex formation. This is followed by a chapter devoted to the bonding and energetics of bond formation, which discusses the various theories relating to the formation of molecular complexes, particularly the Mulliken–Orgel treatment and the quantum-mechanical interpretation of charge transfer. $\sigma$- and $\pi$-complexes are also considered.

Chapter 3, the largest in the book, deals with methods and techniques used to determine compositions and stabilities of molecular complexes. It contains an extensive review of procedures used for measuring molecular and macroscopic properties that yield information about the characteristic features of molecular complexes. This chapter is followed by one concerned with a discussion of physical properties of the complexes measured by the procedures outlined in the previous chapter, particularly spectra, magnetism and dipole moments. The effect of donor excited states on charge transfer bands is also considered in the light of recent researches. The detailed discussion of the effects of structures of donors and acceptors on complex formation is given in Chapter 5.

The penultimate chapter contains a detailed discussion of the important class of complexes formed by Group III elements with those of Groups V and VI of the Periodic Table, and also with aromatic donors. The molecular complexes formed by boron trifluoride and trichloride are given special attention. The applications of molecular complexes in a large number of fields are shown in Chapter 7, the topics covered ranging from medicine to chemistry in its widest sense.

I wish to record my sincere thanks to those who made this work possible. I am grateful to Professor J. C. Robb and Dr. J. K. Brown of the Chemistry Department of the University of Birmingham. Thanks are due to Dr. M. E. Foss and Dr. W. J. Geary of the Department of Chemistry and Metallurgy of the Lanchester College of Technology, Coventry, and to Dr. A. G. Briggs of the Applied Chemistry Department of the Technological University, Loughborough. I wish to place on record my thanks to my sons, Paul L. Rose, B.A.(Oxon.) of St. Catherine's College, Oxford, and John A. Rose of the University of Birmingham, for their help in literature searches, proof reading and useful comments.

*Blackburn,*                                                      J. ROSE
*August,* 1966

# CHAPTER 1

# INTRODUCTION

THE term molecular or addition complex embraces a wide variety of diverse substances, ranging from the stable and primarily ionic dative co-ordination compounds, such as those formed between ammonia and boron trifluoride[1] or triethylamine and iodine,[2] to the weak self-complexes of benzene or nitroaniline.[3] Between these two extremes there is a considerable range of intermediate interaction products, e.g. the complexes of the transition metals and $\pi$-bonded systems, such as olefins,[4] or those formed between aromatic compounds with the halogens.[5] Molecular complexes are quite different from the clathrate and occlusion adducts, e.g. nickel cyanide–ammonia–benzene or methanol–hydroquinone species, in which there is no donor–acceptor interaction.[6] Moreover, complexes formed by intramolecular charge transfer or charge relocalization transitions[1] are not included in this review, though they give rise to very intense absorption spectra which are similar to those given by molecular complexes. Thus polyatomic anions, e.g. $SO_4^{2-}$, $ClO_4^-$, $MnO_4^{2-}$ or $CrO_4^{2-}$, which are of the intraionic charge transfer type, are not termed molecular complexes; the same applies to hydrated amines, for which the transition can be expressed in the form [7]

$$X^-(H_2O)_n \xrightarrow{h\nu} X(H_2O)_n^-.$$

It is also worth noting that most of the complexes in the transition-metal chemistry sense are excluded, though they are of the charge-transfer type and give rise to intense absorption spectra, the extinction coefficients of which are of the order of $10^4$. On the other hand, hydrogen-bonded complexes are classified by Mulliken[8] as donor–acceptor species of the molecular complex type, since there is a close analogy between the two classes of complexes.

1

The nature of intermolecular forces between the components in a molecular complex is still obscure and a matter of considerable controversy. The most widely accepted theory is based on the intermolecular charge-transfer concept.[9] This postulates a partial or complete transfer of electrons from the donor to the acceptor and it is known as the donor–acceptor interaction theory. In accordance with this theory, the wave functions of the whole range of molecular complexes may be represented by a single equation incorporating three parameters, the values of which will depend on the type of moieties.[10] Because of the complex nature of the bonds in molecular complexes it is convenient to write the formulae in the form "acceptor–donor" (or vice versa), the long hyphen (−) merely denoting interaction between the two components without reference to the actual structure of the complex.

Pfeiffer[11] was the first to show that certain aromatic hydrocarbons and their derivatives can combine with a variety of organic and inorganic compounds to form molecular complexes.[12] Some of the complexes thus formed were found to be stable and their composition could be represented by a molar ratio 1:1. Pfeiffer assumed that in the case of aromatic reactants the bond arose as a result of unsaturated secondary valencies present in the aromatic nucleus. On the other hand, Lewis[13] considered these complexes in terms of the acid–base theory. It is now believed that these complexes are of the electron donor–acceptor type, in which the aromatic nucleus donates and shares a negative charge ($\pi$-electrons) with the acceptor molecule, such as maleic anhydride, quinones, or polynitro-aromatic compounds.[14]

An important class of molecular complexes is that formed by the interaction of halogens with aromatic compounds. Lachman[15] was the first to initiate this line of work by showing that iodine dissolved in alcohols and ethers to give brown solutions, while solutions of the halogen in aliphatic hydrocarbons or carbon tetrachloride were violet. This study was extended by Hildebrand and Glascock,[16] who showed by a cryoscopic method that iodine formed a co-ordination complex with the aromatic solvent in the brown solution, viz.

$$C_2H_5OH + I_2 \rightleftharpoons C_2H_5OH \cdot I_2.$$

The equilibrium constant of the above reaction at 25° C in carbon tetrachloride was found to be 1·25 l./mole. This was in agreement with Beckmann's observation that the dissolved iodine molecules were present in a diatomic state in the brown solutions, so that the colour was not due to more complex aggregates of the halogen.[17] This and other evidence[18] indicates complex formation in the brown solutions of iodine. It is interesting to note in this connection that the colour of iodine solutions in various media is not directly related to the dipole moments of the solvents. Thus, the apparently polar chloroform gives a violet solution with iodine, while polar ethanol forms a brown solution. On the other hand, non-polar benzene gives a brown solution.

These studies of iodine solutions were extended to inter-halogen compounds.[19] It was found that in solvents in which iodine is brown, iodine chloride is yellow and iodine bromide is yellow to orange, while in carbon tetrachloride — which gives rise to a violet solution of iodine — the colours of the interhalogen solutes are reddish-brown to red.

In general, complex formation takes place in solution and it is difficult to obtain solid molecular complexes. A number of solid complexes have, however, been prepared. For example, the solid products of interaction between trimethylamine and boron trifluoride or trichloride have been investigated by means of infrared and Raman spectra,[33] while pyrene has been found to form solid molecular complexes with 1,4-benzoquinone and its derivatives, particularly the tetrahalo compounds.[34]

There have been substantial developments in the study of molecular complexes in the last two decades, and the gathering momentum of research into this branch of complex formation is reflected by the ever increasing number of reviews and papers. In addition to the books by Pfeiffer[11] and Briegleb,[20] several detailed reviews have been published, which deal with the major aspects of the subject (McGlynn[10]);[21] a book containing expanded review articles was published[22] in 1963. The spectroscopy of molecular complexes has been the subject of many papers, notably those by Orgel,[21] McGlynn,[10] Briegleb,[23] Mason,[24] Murrell,[25] and in the *Annual Reviews of Physical Chemistry*.[26] The experimental techniques used in the study of molecular complex formation have been discussed by Andrews[21] and Booth;[27] Terenin[21] and Tsubomura[28] summarized the subject in Russian and Japanese, respectively. The biological applications of molecular complexes have been considered by McGlynn[29] and Szent-Györgyi,[30] while Andrews and Keefer[31] have reviewed the molecular complexes of the halogens. The chemistry of the complexes formed by the compounds of the Group III elements of the Periodic Table, particularly that of boron, has received considerable attention because of the widespread synthetic and catalytic uses of the interaction products[10, 21, 23, 32] (ref. 21 only concerns the review by Gerrard and Lappert). Extensive reviews, containing considerable numbers of references, have been compiled by Andrews[21] (331 references), Czekalla[23] (58 references) and Stone[21] (109 references). The spectra of molecular complexes were reviewed by Terenin[21] (147 references). The large field of the 1 : 1 complexes is covered by Briegleb's latest book[20] of 280 pages; 600 authors are cited in its index. The topics not fully covered by Briegleb are critically examined and supplemented by Mulliken and Person,[8] who refer to 93 different sources.

## References

1. R. S. MULLIKEN, *J. Amer. Chem. Soc.*, 1952, **74**, 811.
2. H. TSUBOMURA and S. NAGAKURA, *J. Chem. Phys.*, 1957, **27**, 819.
3. C. A. COULSON and P. L. DAVIES, *Trans. Faraday Soc.*, 1952, **48**, 777; S. C. ABRAHAMS, *J. Amer. Chem. Soc.*, 1952, **74**, 2693; K. E. SHULER, *J. Chem. Phys.*, 1952, **20**, 1865; id. ibid , 1953, **21**, 765; H. MURAKAMI, *Bull. Chem. Soc. Japan*, 1953, **26**, 441, 446; also ref. 1.
4. J. CHATT and L. M. VENANZI, *J. Chem. Soc.*, 1957, 4735; J. CHATT *et al.*, ibid., 1957, 2496, 3414; S. C. ABRAHAMS, ref. 3.
5. H. J. EMELÉUS and A. G. SHARPE, *Advances in Inorganic Chemistry and Radiochemistry*, vol. 3., p. 112, Acad. Press, New York, 1961.
6. F. CRAMER, *Z. Angew. Chem.*, 1952, **64**, 437.
7. E. RABINOWITCH, *Rev. Mod. Phys.*, 1942, **14**, 112.
8. R. S. MULLIKEN and W. B. PERSON, *Ann. Rev. Phys. Chem.*, 1962, **13**, 107.
9. R. S. MULLIKEN, *Rec. Trav. Chim.*, 1956, **75**, 845.
10. S. P. McGLYNN, *Chem. Revs.*, 1958, **58**, 1113.
11. P. PFEIFFER, *Organische Molekülverbindungen*, 2nd ed., F. ENKE, Stuttgart, 1937.
12. A. E. HILL, *J. Amer. Chem. Soc.*, 1922, **44**, 1163; C. MAZZETTI and F. DE CARTI, *Gazz. Chim. Ital.*, 1926, **56**, 34.
13. G. N. LEWIS, *J. Franklin Institute*, 1938, **226**, 293.
14. R. S. MULLIKEN, *J. Phys. Chem.*, 1952, **56**, 801.

15. A. LACHMAN, *J. Amer. Chem. Soc.*, 1903, **25**, 50; F. H. GETMAN, ibid., 1928, **50**, 2883.
16. J. H. HILDEBRAND and B. L. GLASCOCK, *J. Amer. Chem. Soc.*, 1909, **31**, 26.
17 E. BECKMANN, *Ann.*, 1909, **367**, 295.
18. J. H. HILDEBRAND and C. A. JENKS, *J. Amer. Chem. Soc.*, 1920, **42**, 2180; J. H. HILDEBRAND and R. L. SCOTT, *Solubility of Non-Electrolytes*, 3rd ed., Reinholds Publ. Co., New York, 1950, p. 272; J. KLEINBERG and A. W. DAVIDSON, *Chem. Revs.*, 1948, **42**, 601; H. A. BENESI and J. H. HILDEBRAND, *J. Amer. Chem. Soc.*, 1948, **70**, 2832; id. ibid., 1949, **71**, 270; R. S. MULLIKEN, ibid., 1950, **72**, 600.
19. A. E. GILLAM, *Trans. Faraday Soc.*, 1933, **29**, 1132; A. E. GILLAM and R. A. MORTON, *Proc. Roy. Soc. (London)*, 1931, **A132**, 152.
20. G. BRIEGLEB, *Zwischenmolekülare Kräfte*, G. BRAUN, Karlsruhe, 1949; id., *Elektronen-Donator-Acceptor-Komplexe*, Springer-Verlag, Berlin, 1961.
21. M. J. S. DEWAR, *Bull. Soc. Chim. France*, 1951, **18**, C. 71; L. J. ANDREWS, *Chem. Revs.*, 1954, **54**, 713; L. E. ORGEL, *Quart. Revs. (London)*, 1954, **8**, 422; A. N. TERENIN, *Uspekh. Khim.*, 1955, **24**, 121; W. GERRARD and M. F. LAPPERT, *Chem. Revs.*, 1958, **58**, 1081; F. G. A. STONE, ibid., 1958, **58**, 101; SANG UP CHOI, *Hwahak Kwa Kongop Ui Chinbo (Korean)*, 1964, **4**, 123.
22. I. LINDQUIST, *Inorganic Adduct Compounds of Oxo-Compounds*, Springer-Verlag, Berlin, 1963.
23. G. BRIEGLEB and J. CZEKALLA, *Z. Angew. Chem.*, 1960, **72**, 401.
24. S. F. MASON, *Quart. Revs. (London)*, 1961, **15**, 287.
25. J N. MURRELL, *Quart. Revs. (London)*, 1961, **15**, 191.
26. J. R. PLATT, *Ann. Rev. Phys. Chem.*, 1959, **10**, 349; W. C. PRICE, ibid., 1960, **11**, 133; D. A. RAMSAY, ibid., 1961, **12**, 255.
27. D. BOOTH, *Sci. Progress*, 1960, **48**, 435; also L. J. ANDREWS, ref. 21.
28. H. TSUBOMURA and A. KUBOYAMA, *Kagaku to Kogyo (Tokyo)*, 1961, **14**, 537.
29. S. P. MCGLYNN, *Radiation Research (Suppl.)*, 1960, **2**, 300.
30. A. SZENT-GYÖRGYI, *Introduction to Submolecular Biology*, Acad. Press, New York, 1960.
31. L. J. ANDREWS and R. M. KEEFER, *Advances in Inorganic Chemistry and Radiochemistry*, vol. 3, Acad. Press, New York, 1961.
32. D. R. MARTIN, *Chem. Revs.*, 1944, **34**, 461; id. ibid., 1948, **42**, 581; R. S. MULLIKEN, *Symp. on Modern Phys.*, Nikko, Japan, 1953, 45; N. N. GREENWOOD and R. L. MARTIN, *Quart. Revs. (London)*, 1954, **8**, 1; A. B. BURG, *Rec. Chem. Progr.*, Kresge-Hooker Sci. Lib., 1954, **15**, 159; F. G. A. STONE, *Quart. Revs. (London)*, 1955, **9**, 174; M. F. LAPPERT, *Chem. Revs.*, 1956, **56**, 959; W. TRZEBIATOWSKI, *Rep. 2nd. Conf. Theoret. Chem. Warsaw*, 1956, 69; O. HASSELL, *Proc. Roy. Soc. (London)*, 1957, 250; YA. M. SLOBODIN, *Proisdvodstwo Smazochnykh Materialov*, 1959, No. 5, 63; O. HASSELL, *Svensk Kem. Tidskr.*, 1960, **72**, 88; H. S. BOOTH and D. R. MARTIN, *Boron Trifluoride and its Derivatives*, Wiley, New York, 1949; A. V. TOPCHIEV *et al.*, *Boron Fluoride and its Compounds as Catalysts in Organic Chemistry*, Pergamon Press, London, 1959; H. C. BROWN and P. A. TIERNEY, *J. Inorg. Nucl. Chem.*, 1959, **9**, 51.
33. R. L. AMSTER and R. C. TAYLOR, *Spectrochimica Acta*, 1964, **20**, 1487.
34. B. TURCSANYI and F. TUDOS, *Magy. Kem. Folyoirat*, 1965, **71**, 39.

# CHAPTER 2

# BONDING AND ENERGETICS OF BOND FORMATION IN MOLECULAR COMPLEXES

INTENSIVE studies of molecular complexes revealed a number of characteristic features, notably the following:

(1) The equilibria involved in the formation of molecular complexes are established very rapidly. Indeed, very few reactions proceed at a measurable rate to permit kinetic studies.[1]

(2) The distances separating the donor and acceptor moieties in crystalline addition complexes are very much greater than those corresponding to covalent bonds.[2] They are also very much less than those expected from van der Waals interactions.

(3) Addition complexes are formed in simple molecular ratios and are, in general, highly coloured. Several exceptions occur,[3] however, and in many cases there is no correlation between the dipole moments of the acceptors and the colours of their molecular complexes with specific donors.[4]

(4) The stability of many molecular complexes is related to both ionization potential of the donor and the electron affinity of the acceptor[4,5] (also see p. 10).

(5) In the case of many molecular complexes formed by the combination of nitro-compounds, e.g. s-trinitrobenzene, with aromatic hydrocarbons, the heat liberated on formation of the 1:1 product decreases with changes in polarizability of the hydrocarbon component in the order[6]

Anthracene > phenanthrene > naphthalene > benzene.

(6) Many substances, which lack partial moments though they are susceptible to polarization, e.g. iodine, form fairly stable addition complexes with aromatic hydrocarbons.[7]

In view of the above experimental evidence, the concept of covalent bonding between the donor and acceptor moieties, as

6

originally postulated[7] does not seem to be valid [see (1) and (2) above], and various theories of bonding have been postulated. The observed trends in the heat of formation [see (5) above] appear to indicate, according to Briegleb, that certain addition complexes are formed as a result of electrostatic attraction between molecules with permanent dipoles and non-polar species in which polarizability can be induced,[8] e.g. products of interaction between aromatic hydrocarbons or amines with nitro-compounds,[9] iodine,[10] chloranil,[11] malic acid[12] and sulphur dioxide.[13]

A modification of the above polarization theory of Briegleb emphasizes the effect of partial and non-overall moments of the acceptors on the stability of the complex.[14] This hypothesis is subject, however, to serious strictures [see (6)]. It should also be noted that the Briegleb bonding form would probably not involve sufficient transfer between donor and acceptor to cause the marked changes in light absorption which accompany complex formation,[15] especially in the case of aromatic nitro complexes [see (3)]. To meet this difficulty, it has been postulated[16,17] that collisions between suitably oriented molecules in solution bring about a drift of electrons from one component to another. This drift is supposed to be enhanced by greater frequency of collision and deeper intermolecular penetration. For example, the colours of solutions of aromatic amines in nitro-aromatic compounds are intensified, when the temperature is raised, provided the volume is kept constant; a similar result is obtained when the hydrostatic pressure is raised at a constant temperature.[16,18] In certain cases, however, non-colour producing London interactions or those of the Briegleb type occur to a significant extent. For instance, spectrophotometric studies show no evidence of complex formation between picric acid and s-trinitrobenzene,[3] whereas partition studies[19] point to a strong interaction between these compounds. Similar considerations apply to the naphthalene–picric acid interaction.

The above theory of electronic drift in intermolecular collisions was taken a stage further by Weiss, who postulated a transfer of an electron from the donor to the acceptor, i.e. an intermolecular semipolar bond, viz.

$$D: + A \rightarrow [D\cdot]^+[\cdot A]^-.$$

The intense colours of various addition complexes are thus ascribed to the odd electron molecules which, in general, require only low excitational energies.[5,20] This concept is supported by observations concerning the effect of ionization potentials of donors and electron affinities of acceptors [see (4)]. However, the heats of formation in nitro or quinoid complexes are much too low for salt formation.[21] This conflict of evidence has led Brackmann[22] to consider the complex structure as a resonance hybrid to which no-bond and dative forms contribute, i.e.

$$D:A \leftrightarrow D^+:A^-.$$

This view is somewhat supported by the study of the crystal structures of quinhydrone (J. S. Anderson[2]) and $p$-iodoaniline (H. M. Powell *et al.*[2]) aromatic complexes. Furthermore, infrared spectra of molecular complexes of benzene involving bromine as an acceptor support resonance between the structures,[23] viz.

$$D\!-\!\!\!-\!\!\!-\!X-Y \leftrightarrow (D-X^+)+Y^-.$$

Similar considerations apply to the complexes formed between picric acid and aromatic hydrocarbons, such as stilbene, anthracene and naphthalene.[24] On this basis the colour of a molecular complex is a characteristic feature of the complex itself. To some extent this theory is related to the intermolecular collision theory.[15,16,17] Similarly, the relation between colour and resonance of the complex forms an important part of Mulliken's theory of bonding in charge-transfer complexes.[4,25]

### The Mulliken charge-transfer or donor–acceptor theory

The Mulliken theory is concerned with intermolecular change-transfer. Mulliken termed substances formed as a result of such transition charge-transfer complexes — a rather wide description, which is used without discrimination.[26,27] The term charge-transfer has really only an absolute meaning when used as a label for an electronic transition that is accompanied by a migration of charge from one molecule to another. Hence, the term has no significance if, for example, the ground state of a complex is described by molecular orbital theory; the label, charge-transfer, is, however, useful when describing a transfer of charge from a donor to an acceptor. As far as the complexes involved are concerned, the Mulliken theory applies in the first place to the range of substances described in Chapter 1, though the concept of charge-transfer has been extended to inorganic species of stable complexes and chelates.

In the intermolecular transitions there is a complete or partial electron transfer from one component of the complex to another, and the formation of the substance is usually accompanied by a new characteristic absorption band designated as an intermolecular charge-transfer spectrum. The Mulliken treatment only applies to cases in which the donor and acceptor are neutral closed-shell species and are both in symmetrical singlet electronic states. The charge-transfer forces have orientational properties, so that complexes are formed in simple molecular ratios (*vide* 3). Furthermore, these orientational properties have been confirmed by the study of crystal structure of numerous molecular complexes,[2,28] which indicates that the component molecules are stacked one above the other in parallel planes with little change in the bond distance within the donor and acceptor species. For instance, a 1 : 1 complex is formed between 9-$p$-dimethylaminostyrylacridine and 10-ethyl-9-$\beta$-carbomethoxyethylacridinium iodide by the association of the two flat molecules by means of an exoelectronic bond acting perpendicularly to the molecular planes.[29]

Another relevant example concerns the benzene–chlorine complex, in which according to Mulliken,[30] the electron goes into an antibonding molecular orbital of the acceptor. The study of the absorption band at 526 cm$^{-1}$ of this loose charge-transfer complex shows that one chlorine atom is above the C—C bond, while the other chlorine atom is above the middle of the ring and outside it. The Cl–Cl axis does not coincide with the sixfold axes of benzene and it is not parallel to the plane of the aromatic compound; this non-symmetry gives rise to the 526 cm$^{-1}$ band. It is also interesting to note in this connection that charge-transfer forces in molecular complexes are largest if one molecule is laterally translated by some bond lengths with respect to the other, so that the bond energy is greater than the dispersion energy at normal separating distances in the complex (*vide* S. Aono, ref. 55, 1958).

Investigations of dichroism of crystalline complexes[31] and the intensifications of the colours observed on compressing solutions of aniline and nitrobenzene support the Mulliken concept.[16] Moreover, the observed magnitudes of the dipole moments of aromatic–iodine complexes can be ascribed to the partial ionic character of the Mulliken bond.[32] Other observations supporting the charge-transfer theory are as follows:

(a) A linear relation exists between the charge-transfer absorption frequencies and ionization potentials of several donor molecules in iodine complexes (see also pp. 94–98, Chapter 4). It is possible to determine the ionization potentials of donors by using the frequencies of charge-transfer bands in their complexes with a series of acceptors.[33] For instance, the ionization potential of the donor hexamethylbenzene is found to be about 8·6 eV, using the absorption spectra of the chloroform solutions of complexes containing the acceptors tetracyanoethylene[34] (at 561 m$\mu$), 2,3-dicyanobenzoquinone[35] (at 460 m$\mu$), or 2,3-dicyano-5,6-dichlorobenzoquinone[33,35] (at 487 m$\mu$). In terms of the Mulliken theory the energy required for the transition from the ground to the excited state, which gives rise to the intense absorption spectrum, depends *in part* on the energy required to transfer the electron density from the donor to the acceptor; this, in turn, depends on the ionization potential of the donor and the electron affinity of the acceptor.[25,33] Excellent correlation also exists between the ionization potentials of donors and stabilities of various charge-transfer complexes.[4,24,25,33,42,44,65]

(b) There exists a linear relationship between the extinction coefficients at the absorption maxima of the complexes and the reciprocal of the cube root of the stability constants,[36] e.g. in iodine–methylbenzene systems. Similar considerations apply to benzene adducts of halogens, interhalogens, sulphur dioxide and *s*-trinitrobenzene,[33] as predicted by theory.

(c) A plot of the minimum localization energy of the donor versus the frequency of the maximum absorption of the complex is linear in the case of *p*-chloranil–polycyclic aromatic hydrocarbon complexes;[37] this can be interpreted in terms of Mulliken's theory.

(d) The pronounced ultraviolet absorption maximum at about 300 m$\mu$ of the solutions of halogens or sulphur dioxide in certain aromatic solvents[38] or in complexes of aromatic substances with maleic anhydride[12] relates to the addition complex as a whole and not to the aromatic moiety only.

(e) For a number of polynuclear aromatic hydrocarbons the quenching efficiencies of fluorescence by methylated benzenes are in the order benzene < toluene < xylene < mesitylene. This is also the sequence in which the ionization energies of these solvents decrease, in agreement with the charge-transfer theory.[39]

(f) Fluorescence, reflectance and absorption spectra of the products of interaction of hexamethylbenzene with chloranil, 1,3,5-trinitrobenzene and aromatic hydrocarbons with tetrachlorophthalic anhydride point to charge-transfer transitions. Thus, the photoluminescence of crystalline complexes of hexamethylbenzene with chloranil is a charge-transfer fluorescence.[40]

(g) The absorption spectra of the complexes formed between ether and certain chlorides, e.g. aluminium, zinc and titanium chlorides, or between n-heptane and the chlorides of aluminium, stannous tin and ferric iron appear to be due to intermolecular charge-transfer transitions.[41]

(h) The emission and absorption spectra of complexes formed between aromatic hydrocarbons as donors and 1,3,5-trinitrobenzene or trimesic acid as acceptors are mirror-symmetric, the emission spectra being charge-transfer luminescent in character. This mirror-symmetry is still preserved in propyl ether–isopentane glass at −190°C.[42]

(i) In solutions of organic molecular complexes the contribution of resonance types of interaction to intermolecular charge-transfer spectra is very small;[43] dipole–induced dipole interactions predominate. In the case of complexes formed between polynitrobenzenes and polynuclear aromatic hydrocarbons the electrostatic attraction is nearly all of the dipole–induced dipole type. There is no correlation, however, between the dipole moment of acceptors, such as nitromethane or nitrobenzene, and the absorption spectrum of the complex involving specific donors.

### The quantum-mechanical interpretation of the charge-transfer theory

Mulliken put the idea of charge-transfer into the language of quantum mechanics.[4, 25, 44] In terms of the Mulliken theory, the interaction of the no-bond ground state $\Psi_0(DA)$ and the polar excited state $\Psi_1(D^+A^-)$ was considered to produce a stabilized ground state having a wave function $\Psi_0'$ given by the expression

$$\Psi_0' = \Psi_0(DA) + \lambda\Psi_1(D^+A^-)$$

and an excited state (charge-transfer state) having a wave function

$$\Psi_1' = \Psi_1(D^+A^-) + \mu\Psi_0(DA).$$

The coefficients $\lambda$ and $\mu$ are generally small compared with unity. The charge-transfer band of the complex was considered by Mulliken to be associated with the electron transition

$$\Psi_0' \rightarrow \Psi_1'.$$

The above treatment may be extended to include a third term corresponding to the structure $(D^-A^+)$, the wave function being $\Psi_2$.

Another terminology, involving coefficients $a$, $b$ and $c$, instead of $\lambda$ and $\mu$, has also been used to express the charge-transfer theory in terms of quantum mechanics. Here the wave function of the molecular complex $\Psi_N(DA)$, when the donor $D$ (a weak base) and acceptor $A$ (a weak acid) are in their symmetrical ground states, is given by the equation

$$(2.1) \quad \Psi_N(DA) = a\Psi_0(DA) + b\Psi_1(D^+A-) + c\Psi_2(D^-A^+),$$

where the no-bond function $\Psi_0$ corresponds to structures in which the binding is effected by classical intermolecular forces (dipole–dipole, dipole–induced dipole, etc.) or London forces; the function $\Psi_1$ refers to the dative bond, which arises when an electron is transferred from $D$ to $A$, so that in addition to the classical forces relating to $\Psi_0$ there are also weak chemical interactions between odd electrons on the two moieties; the wave function $\Psi_2$ corresponds to the structure $D^-A^+$, while $a$, $b$ and $c$ are coefficients such that $c \ll b$ and $b^2/a^2$ is generally very small, e.g. for complexes of ions of transition elements with ethylenic systems.[45] In the case of self-complexes, e.g. benzene–benzene[4, 46] where the donor and acceptor have similar properties, $b = c$. On the other hand, if $A$ is a strong acid and $D$ is a strong base, then $c$ is negligible and the final term in eqn. (2.1) vanishes. In complexes of medium strength,[47] where the acceptor has partial ionic character, the charge-transfer fraction of the transition is measured by $b/a$. By applying the Ritz variation principle[48] the ground state energy $E$ associated with the total wave function of the complex is given by the relation.

(2.2) $$(W_0 - E)(W_1 - E) = (H_{01} - ES)^2,$$

where the energy $W_0$ associated with the structure $DA$ is given by

$$W_0 = \int \Psi_0 H \Psi_0 \, d\tau,$$

the symbol $\int \ldots d\tau$ implies integration over all the coordinates represented in the integrand, while the energy $W_1$ associated with their structure $D^+A^-$ is given by[48]

$$W_1 = \int \Psi_1 H \Psi_1 \, d\tau.$$

In the above equations $H$ is the exact Hamiltonian of an entire set of nuclei and electrons of the complex; the overlap $S$ of the functions corresponding to the structures $DA$ and $D^+A^-$ is given by the relation

$$S = \int \Psi_1 \Psi_0 \, d\tau$$

while the interaction energy $H_{01}$ of $DA$ and $D^+A^-$ is represented by

$$H_{01} = \int \Psi_1 H \Psi_0 \, d\tau.$$

Since the ground state energy $E$ may be expressed in the form

$$E \equiv W_N \approx W_0$$

so that

$$W_1 - E \approx W_1 - W_0,$$

it follows that

(2.3) $\qquad E \equiv W_N = W_0 - (H_{01} - W_0 S)^2/(W_1 - W_0),$

where $W_N$ is the associated ground state wave function of the complex. The corresponding energy $W_E$ of the excited structure $(W_E \approx W_1)$ is, therefore, given by

$$W_E = W_1 + (H_{01} - W_1 S)^2/(W_1 - W_0),$$

the relevant wave function being

(2.4) $\qquad \Psi_E = a^* \Psi_1(D^+ A^-) - b^* \Psi_0(DA)$

so that a characteristic intermolecular charge-transfer spectrum results.[4] It can also be shown that the coefficients $a$ and $b$ of the ground state, and $a^*$ and $b^*$ of the excited state are given by

(2.5) $\qquad \left(\dfrac{b}{a}\right)_{\text{ground}} = -(H_{01} - SW_0)/(W_1 - W_0)$

and

(2.6) $\qquad \left(\dfrac{b^*}{a^*}\right)_{\text{excited}} = -(H_{01} - SW_1)/(W_1 - W_0),$

where the ground state resonance energy $(W_0 - W_N)$ is about 0–10 kcal/mole; it is, for example, about 1·3 kcal/mole for the benzene–iodine complex. In weak molecular complexes $S$, $H_0$ and $(W_0 - W_N)$ are quite small, while $a^* \approx a \approx 1$ and $b^* \approx b \approx 0$, but $(W_1 - W_0)$ is large, e.g. for the above benzene–iodine complex the energy difference is about 180 kcal/mole.

The above mathematical treatment can be further developed by noting that if the donor and acceptor species are in their singlet ground states, i.e. they have closed-shell atomic orbitals, then

$$S = \sqrt{2}.S_{DA}/(1 + S^2{}_{DA})^{1/2},$$

where

(2.7) $\qquad S_{DA} = \int \Psi_D \Psi_A \, d\tau$

is the overlap integral; the functions $\Psi_D$ and $\Psi_A$ refer to the highest-energy filled and lowest-energy unfilled orbital of the donor and the excited acceptor, respectively (if $S_{DA} = 0$, $b = 0$ and there is no interaction).

Now the partners in a complex will tend to assume a relative orientation such as to make $S$ and $S_{DA}$ a maximum (R. S. Mulliken, ref. 25). This orientation principle is valid if $c$ in eqn. (2.1) is negligible and if the charge-transfer interaction gives primary stabilizing energy of the ground state of the complex. A detailed discussion of the theoretical aspects of spectral intensities is given in Chapter 4 in the context of the review of the spectral characteristics of molecular complexes.

Another point to be noted is that it is possible to evaluate relative electron affinities $E(A)$ of the acceptors from charge-transfer spectra,[49] since the maximum of the charge-transfer band is given by

$$(2.8) \qquad h\nu = I(D) - E(A) + \Psi_{AD},$$

where $I(D)$ is the ionization potential of the donor. Hence for two molecules of the acceptors $i$ and $j$, we have

$$E(A_i) - E(A_j) = h\nu_j - h\nu_i + \Psi_D - \Psi_D$$

$$(2.9) \qquad\qquad \approx h\nu_j - h\nu_i.$$

For instance,[50] in the case of the complexes of tetrachlorophthalic anhydride with seven donors, and of 1,3,5-trinitrobenzene with fourteen donors, the electron affinity of the former was found to be $-0 \cdot 03 \pm 0 \cdot 01$ and $+0 \cdot 06 \pm 0 \cdot 13$ (eV) for the latter, all values being relative to the electron affinity of iodine ($1 \cdot 8$ eV).[51]

The application of the quantal treatment can be illustrated by reference to the benzene–iodine complex, though some complications arise here as a result of the existence of contact charge-transfer (see pp. 88–89, Chapter 4). The ground state molecular orbital configuration of the iodine molecule is

$$\ldots \sigma_g(5s)^2 \bar{\sigma}_u(5s)^2 \sigma_g(5p_z)^2 \pi_u(5p_x, 5p_y)^4 \bar{\pi}_g(5p_x, 5p_y)^4,$$

so that if iodine acts as an acceptor, the additional electron enters the $\sigma_u(5p_z)$ antibonding molecular orbital which corresponds to $\Psi_A$ in eqn. (2.7); the bar refers to antibonding character. In the case of the benzene moiety of the complex the $\pi$-molecular orbitals of the aromatic compound are formed from six $2p_z$ atomic orbitals of the six carbon atoms, since benzene has six $\pi$-electrons. Hence the ground state molecular orbital configuration of benzene is

$$\ldots (a_{2u})^2(e_{1g})^4 A_{1g}.$$

The orbital involved in the event of a compound acting as a donor is $e_{1g}$ [corresponding to the $\Psi_D$ function of eqn. (2.7)], so that for complex formation between iodine and benzene the overlap

$$\int \Psi e_{1g} \Psi \bar{\sigma}_u (5p_z) \, d\tau$$

is the maximum (resonance of the dative and no-bonding structures). The most probable model postulated by Mulliken[4] is

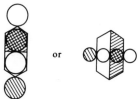

$R_y(C_{2V})$                                                            $R_x(C_{2V}).$

In the $R_y$ model the iodine is rotated through 90° and 30° about the $z$-axis of benzene, while in the $R_x$ model the $z$-axis is parallel to and above the $y$-axis of the aromatic compound (hatching denotes a negative wave function, while cross-hatching refers to a region of overlap of two negative wave functions, which make a *positive* contribution to the overlap integral; total whiteness corresponds to the overlap of two positive wave functions, which also make a *positive* contribution to the overlap integral).

It should be noted, however, that other models are also possible, but certain evidence indicates that the models $R_y$ and $R_x$ predominate in any mixture of isomers at equilibrium. Thus, X-ray diffraction shows that iodine is less symmetrically located than it would be in the case of the $R_y$ and $R_x$ models.[52] Spectrophotometric studies at high pressures also point to the existence of several geometric species of the iodine−benzene complex,[16,53] while infrared evidence is ambiguous.[54]

It is interesting to note that in the $R_x$ and $R_y$ models the interionic attraction in the dative-bond form ($B^+$ and $I_2^-$) is large, while in a similar structure $R'$ ($C_2$), in which the iodine is rotated about the $z$-axis of benzene by an angle different from 30° or an integral multiple of 30°, the overlap is very much less. There is still less overlap in an $E_x$ structure, in which the $z$-axis of iodine is perpendicular to the plane of the benzene molecule, the centre of the $I-I$ bond being on the $x$-axis of the aromatic moiety and distant by about 3Å from the side of the benzenoid hexagon (the centres of charges in the dative-bond structure are too far apart, hence the reduced interaction).

Another additional possibility is an $A$ structure ($C_{6V}$) in which the $z$-axis of benzene coincides with the $z$-axis of iodine, the latter molecule being above the benzene ring; in this case there is no overlap, while for the other models the total overlap is finite. The axial model of $C_{6V}$ symmetry for the charge-transfer benzene–iodine complex is favoured by energy considerations based on spectral data.[55]

The quantum-mechanical concept has been applied to other addition complexes, e.g. the benzene–silver ion and benzene–transition ion complexes[4, 25, 56] and the formulated deductions have been confirmed by X-ray analysis; in this case $c = b$.

The symmetry of benzene–positive ion complexes has been studied by Rundle and Corbett[57] in connection with the gallium and silver complexes. For instance, when $Ga_2Cl_4$ is recrystallized from benzene, a stable complex is formed, having the formula $Ga^+[GaCl_4]^-$ in which the univalent gallium cation $Ga^+$ is strongly solvated. Similar considerations apply to $Ga[AlCl_4]$, but not to $Tl[AlCl_4]$. The gallium complex may have hexagonal symmetry, and this is general for the species benzene–$M^+$, where $M$ is an element of Group III in the Periodic Classification in its $+1$ oxidation state. On the other hand, the complex benzene–$AgClO_4$ is asymmetric, as required by theory, the univalent silver cation lying above one of the C—C bonds.

The reasons for this different behaviour between gallium and silver complexes can be seen by considering the benzene–$M^+$ complex with the cation on the benzene axis and so of $C_{6V}$ symmetry. The highest $\pi$-orbitals of the aromatic ring belong to the irreducible representation $e_V$ (doubly degenerate) so that the orbitals of $M^+$ must belong to the same representation. But for the silver ion the lowest acceptor orbital is $s$ belonging to $a$, orthogonal to the upper filled $\pi$-orbitals of the ring. Hence charge-transfer formation is impossible without electronic promotion, and thus the cation must move to a position of lower symmetry. In the case of the univalent gallium ion, however, the lowest acceptor orbitals are $p$, where the degenerate pairs $p_x p_y \cdots e_1$, can accept the highest energy $\pi$-orbitals from the benzene ring. Hence $C_{6V}$ symmetry for benzene–$M^+$ is not excluded, and $Ga^+[GaCl_4]^-$ has pseudo-hexagonal symmetry. The self-complexes of benzene have also been studied,[4, 18, 46, 58] the coefficients of eqn. (2.1) being related by $c = b \ll a$. Other self-complexes treated by means of the charge-transfer theory are those of p-nitroaniline,[59] iodine,[60] N-ethylphenazyl dimer,[61] biphenyl,[62] and of excimers,[63] i.e. excited dimers such as polycyclic aromatic hydrocarbons. On the other hand, the study of strongly ionic molecular complexes formed by the interaction between strong acid and strong bases shows that there is no steric hindrance and the orbitals are strongly directional, so that there is close approach between the partners, and the bond is strong ($b < 0$ and $c \approx 0$), e.g. triethylamine–iodine[64] or ammonia–boron trifluoride[4] complexes.

The discussion of the theory of molecular complexes, especially of the 1:1 variety, is generally carried out in terms of a no-bond structure with dative structures, including at times locally excited forms[65] (resonance-structure method). In an alternative procedure, known as the "whole-complex MO method", the structure of the molecular complex is described in terms of molecular orbitals of the species as a whole, i.e. the molecular orbitals of the entire complex are constructed as linear combinations of donor and acceptor molecular orbitals. For very loose complexes the wave functions involved in the two methods become nearly identical, whereas considerable differences occur in the case of stable complexes. While the resonance method is preferred for a unified treatment of 1:1 complexes, the molecular orbital procedure is desirable for complexes in which a central acceptor atom or cation is surrounded by several donor anions or molecules. Special attention has been devoted to the treatment of $\pi$-complexes in terms of the molecular orbital method[66] (see also Dewar, ref. 21). In particular, Dewar demonstrates a linear relationship between the charge-transfer band frequency and the coefficient $x$ in the Hückel molecular orbital formula $I = \alpha - x\beta$ for the minimum ionization energy $I$ of the aromatic hydrocarbon $\pi$-donors; the slopes of the straight lines thus obtained are nearly unity for weak $\pi$–$\pi$ complexes. This behaviour is similar to that shown by weak complexes, when the energy of the charge-transfer band is plotted against the ionization energy of the donor (see pp. 94–98, Chapter 4). Furthermore, both the resonance and molecular orbital methods show that the resonance interaction, which stabilizes $\pi$–$\pi$ complexes, is always very much weaker than that of the $\pi$–$\sigma$ and $n$–$\sigma$ complexes.[67]

*Bonding in addition complexes of elements of Group III of the Periodic Table (Thermodynamic treatment)*

The metals ($M$) of Group III as metallic halides $MX_3$ are capable of acting as electron acceptors since the bonding electrons occupy three $ns\ p^2$ hybrid orbitals ($\sigma$-bond) mutually inclined at 120°, thus leaving a partially or totally vacant $np_x$ orbital perpendicular to the place containing the three $\sigma$-bonds; the metal $M$ is thus classified as an acceptor of electrons from a donor and thus as a Lewis acid.[68] The Lewis theory gives no information, however, about the energetics or bond stabilities of the linkages involved, especially since dative bonds are weaker than covalent links because of differences in hybridization.[69]

Thermodynamically, the formation of a solid or liquid donor–$MX_3$ complex in its standard state can be envisaged as follows:

$$D(g) + MX_3(g) \xleftarrow{\Delta G_A} D(g) + MX_3\ (g) \xleftarrow{\Delta G_V} D(g) \text{ and } MX_3(g)$$

$$\downarrow \Delta G_G \qquad \text{in standard states (polymeric)}$$

$$\Delta G_T \longrightarrow D.MX_3(g) \xrightarrow{\Delta G_C} \downarrow \Delta G$$

$$D.MX_3 \text{ (solid or liquid in standard states)}$$

$\Delta G$ is the free-energy change involved in the formation of $D.MX_3$ from $MX_3$ and the donor $D$, all in their standard states;

$\Delta G_A$ is the adjustment energy for converting gaseous components to moieties having configurations present in the complex. $\Delta G_C$ is the energy evolved when the gaseous molecular complex condenses to its standard state (liquid or solid); $\Delta G_G$ is the energy change corresponding to the formation of the complex in the gas phase; $\Delta G_T$ is the total energy released in the formation of the gaseous complex from gaseous components; $\Delta G_V$ is the vaporization energy required to convert the gaseous components in their standard states to a gaseous donor and solid acceptor.

It is evident from the above scheme that the molecular complex will not form if the following conditions obtain:

(a) If $\Delta G_A > \Delta G_T$, since then $\Delta G_G > 0$, as in the case of donors or acceptors having large alkyl groups. It must be noted that in most complexes the relation between $\Delta G_A$ and $\Delta G_T$ is subject to electronic and steric influences. The large alkyl groups are responsible for steric hindrance and a complex will not, in general, be formed,[70] as in the case of the halides of boron with certain substituted amines.

(b) The existence of $\pi$-bonding between $M$ and $X$ in $MX_3$ renders $\Delta G_A$ large, since the adjustment for bonding involves the drawing of $M$ out of the $MX_3$ plane to form vacant $sp^3$ orbitals (energy of rehybridization); complex formation will thus become more difficult.

(c) If the standard state of the complex lies far above those of the components,[71] the molecular complex will, in general, not be formed.

(d) There will be considerable difficulties in forming a complex if the acceptor exists as a polymer, so that additional energy will be required for converting the acceptor from the standard to the gaseous state, e.g. complexing of dimeric $AlX_3$ or $Al(CH_3)_3$ with diborane.

It must be noted that all the steps in the above scheme are quite complex and it is therefore, difficult to establish an acidity scale of dative-bond strengths for the Lewis acids and bases.[4]

## $\sigma$- and $\pi$-complexes

If the bond between the acceptor and ring carbon in molecular complexes is of the $sp^3$ type, then the interaction product is termed a σ-complex, e.g. HF–BF$_3$ or HCl–AlCl$_3$ complexes of alkyl benzenes. On the other hand, complexes of *m*-xylene and the less stable mesitylene with hydrogen chloride are of the π-type in which the donor molecule accommodates the acceptor with little loss of resonance energy, i.e. the HCl complexes substituted hydrocarbons.[72] The best criterion for distinguishing σ- and π-complexes lies in the study of changes in *relative magnitudes* of the stabilities of complex with changes in donor substituents. Thus the logarithms of the stabilities of σ-complexes show a satisfactory linear correlation with the logarithms of the rates of halogenation of the hydrocarbon donors.[73] For π-complexes, however, the relevant plots show many abnormalities.

Another interesting fact is that the above σ-complexes are closely related to transition state intermediates in electrophilic aromatic substitution reactions. For example, the protonated structure of the complex formed between toluene and HCl–AlCl$_3$ is depicted in the form[74]

while the yellow complex of anthracene in sulphuric acid[75] may be written in the form

In the former structure the organic cation is stabilized through methyl group hyperconjugation, while the meso position in the latter structure is the preferential site of proton co-ordination, as shown by deuterium tracer experiments.[76] It should be noted, however, that a $\sigma$-complex may have a discrete existence despite its close structural relationship to transition state intermediates in aromatic substitutions, e.g. the pyridine–iodine complexes, which are separated by an energy barrier.[77] Furthermore, the $\sigma$-complexes are highly coloured, and the spectra of aromatic hydrocarbons in HF–BF$_3$ solutions show bands at 400 m$\mu$, which are assumed to point to the existence of aromatic carbonium ions.[78] Similarly, polynuclear hydrocarbons show in HF–BF$_3$ solutions bands at about 480 m$\mu$, which are presumed to be due to protonated structures in which the positive charge is distributed over the entire ring system.

## $n$–$\pi$ complexes

While the acceptor chloranil forms $\pi$–$\pi$ complexes with polycyclic aromatic hydrocarbon donors,[37, 79] where the donated electron forming the complex is a $\pi$-electron, it also gives rise to $n$–$\pi$ interaction products.[80] For instance, on adding glycine or alanine to a $10^{-4}$ M solution of chloranil in 50% aqueous ethanol buffered to a suitable pH, the spectrum of the solution undergoes a marked change,[81] viz. the absorption band at 295 m$\mu$ is reduced and a new band appears at longer wavelengths in the region 330–380 m$\mu$, the actual position depending on pH; this effect is reversed on heating the solution. In addition, there is an approximately linear relation between the reciprocal of the amino-acid concentration and the reciprocal of the optical density of the new band in accordance with Benesi–Hildebrand equation.[82] Similar results are obtained in the case of chloranil-protein complexes in 50% aqueous ethanol, except that the new band lies at shorter wavelengths than in the amino-acid systems. It is also found that the absorption spectra of chloranil–amino acid and chloranil–protein mixtures are very similar to those of chloranil–amine mixtures. These $n$–$\pi$ complexes are probably formed by a lone-pair electron from the nitrogen in the amino group being donated to the chloranil. It must be noted that the normal charge-transfer band has not been observed in these amino-acid complexes, though some aliphatic amines show such a band in carbon tetrachloride solution but not in 50% aqueous ethanol solution. Though similar behaviour is shown by the 1:1 complexes of purines with various hydrocarbons in 50% aqueous ethanol solution,[83] it is thought that they are charge-transfer complexes.[81]

A controversial example of $n-\pi$ complexes is that involving the acceptor iodine.[84] During complex formation the absorption band of free iodine at 520 m$\mu$ shifts to a shorter wavelength in $n-\pi$ charge-transfer species.[85] According to Mulliken (ref. 25, p. 845), the iodine "blue shift" is due to the increased exchange repulsion between iodine and the donor. On the other hand Slifkin (loc. cit.) considers that in very weak molecular complexes there is very little charge-transfer, so that the corresponding absorption band is that of the free acceptor; in strong complexes, however, there is greater charge-transfer and the acceptor becomes, in effect, a negative ion.

Other $n-\pi$ complexes are those formed between aromatic and aliphatic amino acids with oxygen. In these complexes the donated electron is one of the lone pair of the nitrogen atom of the amino group;[86] the changes in the absorption spectra of the steroids when bound to proteins, for example, are consistent[87] with those observed in other systems in which $n-\pi$ charge-transfer occurs.[88] It is also worth noting that the complex formed by the amino-acid tryptophane and riboflavine-5′-phosphate is a $\pi-\pi$ complex.[89]

The concept of lone-pair donors has received a great deal of attention in recent years, though many of the empirical ideas about the behaviour of molecular complexes are based on studies with $\pi$-donors, e.g. benzenes.

In 1961 alone the following studies of $n$-donor–iodine acceptor complexes were reported; sulphides and amides,[88,90] diethyl-ether[91] and sulphur and selenium analogues of 1,4-dioxane.[92] The recent trend in the direction of $n$-donors, i.e. molecules having lone pairs of electrons, is due to the fact that $n$-donor–$\sigma$-acceptor complexes are relatively stable and that the $n$-donor action is largely localized at one atom, contrary to the behaviour of $\pi$-donors; it is thus possible to study more easily the effect of various factors on bonding, especially since the geometrical structures for many complexes containing a $n$-donor moiety are fairly well known. Indeed, recent studies of the $n$-

donor concept brought about a fresh outlook in the field of charge-transfer bands with emphasis on their intensities and energies. For instance, the intensity (integrated molar absorptivity or oscillator strength) of the charge-transfer absorption band of complexes of $n$-donor–iodine acceptor increases with increasing strength of interaction,[88] the latter being measured by the formation constant or enthalpy of formation; here the theory and experimental results agree while the $\pi$-donor–iodine acceptor complexes do not conform to the predicted intensity relation[93] (see also ref. 25, p. 845). It is worth noting, however, that considerable controversy exists as to the exact magnitude of the divergence between experimental data and theoretical predictions for $\pi$-donors[67] especially in the case of weak complexes.

## References

1. D. LL. HAMMICK and G. SIXSMITH, *J. Chem. Soc.*, 1935, 580.
2. J. S. ANDERSON, *Nature*, 1937, **140**, 583; H. M. POWELL *et al.*, *J. Chem. Soc.*, 1943, 153; S. C. WALLWORK and T. T. HARDING, *Nature*, 1953, **171**, 40.
3. S. D. ROSS and I. KUNTZ, *J. Amer. Chem. Soc.*, 1954, **76**, 74.
4. R. S. MULLIKEN, *J. Amer. Chem. Soc.*, 1952, **74**, 811.
5. J. WEISS, *J. Chem. Soc.*, 1942, 245; ibid., 1943, 462.
6. G. BRIEGLEB and T. SCHACHOWSKOY, *Z. phys. Chem.*, 1932, **B19**, 255.
7. L. J. ANDREWS, *Chem. Revs.*, 1954, **54**, 763.
8. G. BRIEGLEB, *Z. phys. Chem.*, 1932, **B16**, 249; id., *Zwischenmolekülare Kräfte*, G. BRAUN, Karlsruhe, Germany, 1949, pp. 13, 55.
9. G. BRIEGLEB, *Z. phys. Chem.*, 1934, **B26**, 63.
10. T. M. CROMWELL and R. L. SCOTT, *J. Amer. Chem. Soc.*, 1950, **72**, 3825; C. VAN DE STOLPE, Thesis, Amsterdam Univ., 1953.
11. O. J. WALKER, *Trans. Faraday Soc.*, 1935, **31**, 432.
12. W. G. BARB, *Trans. Faraday Soc.*, 1953, **49**, 143.
13. W. G. BARB, *Proc. Roy. Soc. (London)*, 1952, **A212**, 66, 177.
14. G. BRIEGLEB and J. KAMBEITZ, *Z. phys. Chem.*, 1934, **B25**, 253; C. J. LeFÈVRE and R. J. W. LeFÈVRE, *J. Chem. Soc.*, 1935, 957; R. J. W. LeFÈVRE, *Trans. Faraday Soc.*, 1937, **33**, 210.
15. D. LL. HAMMICK *et al.*, *J. Chem. Soc.*, 1932, 171.
16. R. E. GIBSON and O. H. LOEFFLER, *J. Amer. Chem. Soc.*, 1940, **62**, 1324.
17. D. LL. HAMMICK and R. B. YULE, *J. Chem. Soc.*, 1940, 1539.
18. H. MURAKAMI, *Bull. Chem. Soc. Japan*, 1953, **26**, 441, 446.
19. T. S. MOORE *et al.*, *J. Chem. Soc.*, 1931, 1447.
20. R. B. WOODWARD, *J. Amer. Chem. Soc.*, 1942, **64**, 3058.
21. M. J. S. DEWAR, *Electronic Theories of Organic Chemistry*, Oxford Univ. Press, 1949; W. S. RAPSON *et al.*, *J. Chem. Soc.*, 1946, 1110.
22. W. BRACKMANN, *Rec. Trav. Chim.*, 1949, **68**, 147.
23. W. B. PERSON *et al.*, *J. Amer. Chem. Soc.*, 1960, **82**, 29.

24. G. BRIEGLEB et al., Z. phys. Chem., 1959, 21, 99.
25. R. S. MULLIKEN, J. Amer. Chem. Soc., 1950, 72, 600, 4493; id., J. Chem. Phys., 1951, 19, 514; id., J. Chim. Phys., 1954, 51, 341; id., J. Chem. Phys., 1955, 23, 397; id., Rec. Trav. Chim., 1956, 75, 845.
26. J. N. MURRELL, J. Chem. Soc., 1956, 3779.
27. J. N. MURRELL, The Theory of the Electronic Spectra of Organic Molecules, Methuen, London, 1963, p. 271.
28. K. NAKAMOTO, J. Amer. Chem. Soc., 1952, 74, 1739; G. HUSE, J. Chem. Soc., 1943, 435.
29. V. A. IZMAILSKII and L. D. VISHNEVSKII, Dokl. Akad. Nauk SSSR, 1958, 121, 111.
30. R. S. MULLIKEN, 1955, ref. 25.
31. K. NAKAMOTO, 1952, ref. 28.
32. F. FAIRBROTHER, J. Chem. Soc., 1948, 1051.
33. H. McCONNELL et al., J. Chem. Phys., 1953, 21, 66.
34. N. G. S. CHAMPION, J. Chem. Soc., 1961, 5060.
35. R. FOSTER, Nature, 1962, 195, 490; id., Tetrahedron, 1960, 10, 96; S. P. McGLYNN and J. D. BOGGUS, J. Amer. Chem. Soc., 1958, 80, 5096; A. BIER, Rec. Trav. Chim., 1956, 75, 866; G. BRIEGLEB and J. CZEKALLA, Z. Elektrochem., 1955, 59, 184; J. A. A. KETELAAR, J. Phys. Radium, 1954, 15, 197.
36. M. TAMRES et al., J. Amer. Chem. Soc., 1953, 75, 4358.
37. W. L. PETICOLAS, J. Chem. Phys., 1957, 26, 429.
38. L. J. ANDREWS and R. M. KEEFER, J. Amer. Chem. Soc., 1951, 73, 4169.
39. K. MAJUMDAR and S. BASU, J. Chem. Phys., 1960, 33, 1199.
40. J. CZEKALLA et al., Z. Elektrochem., 1957, 61, 1053.
41. S. HAYAKAWA, Bull. Chem. Soc. Japan, 1955, 28, 447.
42. J. CZEKALLA et al., Z. Elektrochem., 1959, 63, 623, 712.
43. H. MURAKAMI, Bull. Soc. Chem. Japan, 1954, 27, 268.
44. R. S. MULLIKEN, J. Phys. Chem., 1952, 56, 801.
45. F. BASOLO and R. G. PEARSON, Mechanism of Inorganic Reactions, Wiley, New York, 1958, p. 351; J. CHATT, Nature, 1956, 177, 852.
46. K. E. SHULER, J. Chem. Phys., 1952, 20, 1865; id. ibid., 1953, 21, 765.
47. R. FOSTER and T. THOMSON, Trans. Faraday Soc., 1962, 58, 800.
48. C. A. COULSON, Valence, Clarendon Press, Oxford, 1952, pp. 58–67.
49. G. BRIEGLEB and J. CZEKALLA, Z. anorg. Chem., 1960, 72, 401.
50. M. BATLEY and L. E. LYONS, Nature (London), 1962, 196, 573.
51. J. TORTNER and U. SOKOLOV, Nature (London), 1961, 190, 1003.
52. G. DALLINGA, Acta Cryst., 1954, 7, 665.
53. R. E. GIBSON and O. H. LOEFFLER, J. Amer. Chem. Soc., 1939, 61, 2877; D. L. GLUSKER et al., J. Chem. Phys., 1953, 21, 1407; W. GORDY, ibid., 1939, 7, 93.
54. E. E. FERGUSON, J. Chem. Phys., 1957, 26, 1387; L. W. DAASCH, Symp. on Molecular Structure and Spectra, Ohio State Univ., Columbus, Ohio, June, 1958; E. E. FERGUSON and F. A. MATSEN, J. Chem. Phys., 1958, 29, 105.
55. S. AONO, Progr. Theoret. Phys., Kyoto, 1958, 20, 137; id., ibid., 1959, 22, 313.
56. R. E. RUNDLE and J. H. GORING, J. Amer. Chem. Soc., 1950, 72, 5337; J. CHATT, Nature (London), 1956, 177, 852; id., J. Chem. Soc., 1953, 2939; M. J. S. DEWAR, Bull. Soc. Chim., France, 1951, 18, C. 71.

57. R. E. RUNDLE and J. D. CORBETT, *J. Amer. Chem. Soc.*, 1957, **79**, 757.
58. C. A. COULSON and P. L. DAVIES, *Trans. Faraday Soc.*, 1952, **48**, 777.
59. S. C. ABRAHAMS, *J. Amer. Chem. Soc.*, 1952, **74**, 2693.
60. H. McCONNELL, *J. Chem. Phys.*, 1954, **22**, 760.
61. K. H. HAUSSER and J. N. MURRELL, *J. Chem. Phys.*, 1957, **27**, 500.
62. H. C. LONGUET-HIGGINS and J. N. MURRELL, *Proc. Phys. Soc.*, 1955, **68**, A. 601.
63. R. M. HOCHSTRASSER, *J. Chem. Phys.*, 1962, **36**, 1099; M. A. SLIFKIN, *Nature (London)*, 1963, **200**, 766.
64. H. TSUBOMURA and S. NAGAKURA, *J. Chem. Phys.*, 1957, **27**, 819.
65. G. BRIEGLEB, *Elektronen-Donator-Acceptor-Komplexe*, Springer-Verlag, Berlin, 1961.
66. M. J. S. DEWAR and A. R. LEPLEY, *J. Amer. Chem. Soc.*, 1961, **83**, 4560; M. J. S. DEWAR and H. RODGERS, ibid., 1962, **84**, 395.
67. R. S. MULLIKEN and W. B. PERSON, *Ann. Rev. Phys. Chem.*, 1962, **13**, 107.
68. G. N. LEWIS, *J. Franklin Institute*, 1938, **226**, 293.
69. H. A. SKINNER and N. B. SMITH, *J. Chem. Soc.*, 1953, 4025; F. G. A. STONE, *Chem. Revs.*, 1958, **58**, 103.
70. D. GARVIN and G. B. KISTIAKOWSKY, *J. Chem. Phys.*, 1952, **20**, 105.
71. G. B. KISTIAKOWSKY and R. WILLIAMS, *J. Chem. Phys.*, 1955, **23**, 334.
72. H. C. BROWN and J. D. BRADY, *J. Amer. Chem. Soc.*, 1952, **74**, 3570.
73. F. E. CONDON, *J. Amer. Chem. Soc.*, 1948, **70**, 1963; P. D. B. DE LA MARE and P. W. ROBERTSON, *J. Chem. Soc.*, 1943, 279.
74. D. A. McCAULAY and A. P. LIEN, *J. Amer. Chem. Soc.*, 1951, **73**, 2013.
75. V. GOLD et al., *J. Chem. Soc.*, 1952, 2167; V. GOLD and F. L. TYE, ibid., 1952, 2173.
76. V. GOLD and F. A. LONG, *J. Amer. Chem. Soc.*, 1953, **75**, 4543.
77. YA. K. SYRKIN and K. M. ANISIMOVA, *Dokl. Akad. Nauk SSSR*, 1948, **59**, 1457; R. A. ZINGARO et al., *J. Amer. Chem. Soc.*, 1951, **73**, 88; E. BLASIUS and W. WACHTEL, *Z. anal. Chem.*, 1953, **138**, 106; J. KLEINBERG et al., *J. Amer. Chem. Soc.*, 1953, **75**, 1442; G. KÖRTUM and H. WILSKI, *Z. phys. Chem.*, 1953, **202**, 35.
78. C. REID, *Tech. Rep. Lab. of Mol. Struct. and Spect.*, Dept. of Phys., Univ. of Chicago, part 2, 1952–53, p. 295.
79. R. FOSTER and D. LL. HAMMICK, *J. Chem. Soc.*, 1954, 2685; G. BRIEGLEB and J. CZEKALLA, *Z. Elektrochem.*, 1959, **63**, 6; J. B. BIRKS and M. A. SLIFKIN, *Nature (London)*, 1961, **191**, 761.
80. N. J. SMITH, Ph.D. Thesis, Univ. of Chicago, 1955; S. K. CHAKRABARTY and A. K. CHANDRA, *Naturw.*, 1962, **49**, 206; M. A. SLIFKIN, *Nature (London)*, 1962, **195**, 635.
81. J. B. BIRKS and M. A. SLIFKIN, *Nature (London)*, 1963, **197**, 42; M. A. SLIFKIN, *Spectrochim. Acta*, 1964, **20**, 1543.
82. H. BENESI and J. HILDEBRAND, *J. Amer. Chem. Soc.*, 1949, **71**, 2073.
83. J. BOOTH and E. BOYLAND, *Biochem. Biophys. Acta*, 1953, **12**, 75; J. BOOTH et al., *J. Chem. Soc.*, 1954, 598; DE SANTIS et al., *Nature (London)*, 1961, **191**, 900.
84. M. A. SLIFKIN, *Nature (London)*, 1963, **198**, 1301.
85. R. P. LANG, *J. Amer. Chem. Soc.*, 1962, **84**, 1185.
86. M. A. SLIFKIN, *Nature (London)*, 1962, **193**, 464.
87. V. WESTPHAL and B. D. ASHLEY, *J. Biol. Chem.*, 1962, **237**, 2763.
88. H. TSUBOMURA and R. P. LANG, *J. Amer. Chem. Soc.*, 1961, **83**, 2085.

89. I. ISENBERG and A. SZENT-GYÖRGYI, *Proc. U.S. Natl. Acad. Sci.*, 1958, **44**, 857; M. A. SLIFKIN, *Nature (London)*, 1963, **197**, 275.
90. R. S. DRAGO *et al.*, *J. Amer. Chem. Soc.*, 1961, **83**, 3572; M. GOOD *et al.*, ibid., 1961, **83**, 4329.
91. P. A. D. DE MAINE and P. CARAPELLUCI, *J. Mol. Spectroscopy*, 1961, **7**, 83.
92. J. D. McCULLOUGH and I. C. ZIMMERMANN, *J. Phys. Chem.*, 1961, **65**, 888.
93. L. E. ORGEL and R. S. MULLIKEN, *J. Amer. Chem. Soc.*, 1957, **79**, 4839; J. N. MURRELL, ibid., 1959, **81**, 5037.

# CHAPTER 3

# COMPOSITIONS AND STABILITIES OF MOLECULAR COMPLEXES

THE structures of the molecular complexes have been investigated by a variety of methods involving measurements of physical properties of the substances. These properties fall into two classes: molecular and macroscopic. The former are capable of yielding important information about the composition and stability of complexes, while the latter are generally insufficient *per se* to unravel the structural problems. It is also important to note that many molecular complexes cannot be isolated in the pure state and must be studied in solution.

The molecular properties comprise the following:

(a) *Optical.* These include spectra in the whole electromagnetic range at present accessible to experiment, as well as optical rotatory dispersion and polarimetry. Ultraviolet and visible spectra are being extensively used, since they are concerned with valency and bonding. On the other hand, infrared and Raman spectra yield information about molecular symmetry and the presence of specific groups of atoms, while microwave spectra may elucidate the molecular conformation and sometimes yield data concerning molecular dimensions. Finally, optical rotatory dispersion and polarimetry are of importance in the case of asymmetric molecules.

(b) *Diffraction.* This comprises the various techniques based on electron, neutron and X-ray diffraction and serves as a tool for investigating crystalline structures in the widest sense.

(c) *Resonance.* The most recent developments are those concerned with the application of electron spin resonance, nuclear magnetic resonance, nuclear quadrupole resonance and the resonant absorption of X-rays emitted without recoil in the Mössbauer effect.

(d) *Dipole moments*. The measurements of dipole moments are used for confirming complex formation and studying the ionic nature of the complex.

The macroscopic physical properties used for studying complex formation are as follows:

(a) *Conductance*. In certain cases conductimetric measurements will indicate complex formation, the presence of various types of molecular complexes and ionic dissociation.

(b) *Colligative properties*. Experimental determination of freezing point depression, boiling point elevation and vapour pressure lowering of solvents by solutes may be used to determine the composition and stability of molecular complexes.

(c) *Solubility and distribution*. The former is of importance for the determination of compositions and stabilities of molecular complexes, while the latter has been used for the evaluation of electron-donor capacities of aromatic compounds.

(d) *Magnetic susceptibility*. This property indicates the spin multiplicity of electrons in a metal ion and frequently assists structural assignments.

(e) *Thermal properties*. The study of transition points and Trouton's coefficients is of limited use for investigating structures of molecular complexes. This information is rather scanty because of the special nature of molecular complexes.

(f) *Other properties*. Properties such as refractive index, surface tension and viscosity may indicate the presence of complexes and their molecular size. Kinetic techniques have also been used in this field, but their application is limited.

It is clear that a wide variety of techniques is available for the investigation of the structures of molecular complexes. Unfortunately, the correlation of the results obtained by various procedures for molecular complexes of the same type is poor at times. Moreover, there are only meagre references concerning the application of several methods to a particular complex.

The most important methods are those based on the study of certain physical properties, particularly the spectral characteristics of solutions of molecular complexes. A detailed review of some of these procedures is given below. Detailed results obtained by applying these procedures will be given in Chapter 4.

## 1. Spectrophotometry

The existence of many molecular complexes was first recognized by observing the colour changes produced in solutions containing suitable donor and acceptor species. For instance, certain aromatic hydrocarbons, amines or phenols give intensely coloured solutions when mixed with halogens, carboxylic acids or aromatic nitro-compounds. Thus, iodine gives reddish to brown solutions in complexing aromatic solvents, while *p*-chloranil yields an intensely red solution when mixed with hexamethylbenzene in aqueous ethanol. The absorption bands of these complexes are associated with the transfer of an electron from the donor to the acceptor molecule and are termed charge-transfer spectra. In general, molecular complexes give rise to broad intense absorption spectra in the visible and ultraviolet regions in the spectrum due to electronic transitions. These spectra correspond to the formation of molecular complexes. For example, the optical density of the charge-transfer band at 500 m$\mu$ given by the aqueous ethanol solution of the *p*-chloranil–hexamethylbenzene complex is proportional to the product of the concentrations of the reacting species; hence it is reasonable to assume that the red colour is due to a 1:1 molecular complex.[1] If the complexes are weakly bonded, then the bands are broad and show no vibrational structure.

As regards other spectral features, it is worth noting that the longer the wavelength of the charge-transfer band, the greater the stability of the complex, and the more complete the transfer of the electron from the donor to the acceptor.[2] Furthermore, the shift to longer wavelengths may occur from the ultraviolet into the visible spectrum, while new bands may make their appearance in the ultraviolet and infrared regions as a result of complex formation, e.g. in solutions of quinones in various benzene derivatives,[3] or of *p*-chloranil and hexamethylbenzene in benzene.[1] In general, if the molecular complexes are strongly bonded with specific relative orientations stabilized by a dative form ($D^+-A^-$), then the infrared bands of one or both the components may also be modified. In loosely bonded complexes, however, the vibrational infrared bands are only slightly modified or not changed at all.

Similar observations have been made in the case of the donor–acceptor complexes of oxygen with a wide variety of hydrocarbons.[4] For example, oxygenated solutions of benzene, naphthalene and several monosubstituted benzenes show absorption maxima in the near ultraviolet, which disappear when the oxygen is removed. It is found, in general, that when oxygen is dissolved in hydrocarbon solvents under elevated pressures, a new absorption band appears to the long wavelength side of the first singlet absorption band of the hydrocarbon. A similar effect is noted when oxygen is dissolved under high pressure (2,000 lb/cm$^2$) in concentrated solutions of some amino acids, e.g. glycine, alanine or tryptophane.[5] In all cases, the addition of the gas causes a reversible increase in the ultraviolet absorption of the solutions.

An important case is that of a solution of iodine in benzene. This displays a high intensity absorption peak at 290 m$\mu$, which is absent in the spectrum of iodine in the inert, i.e. non-complexing, carbon tetrachloride.[6] It must also be noted in connection with the above benzene or carbon tetrachloride solutions of the halogen that the absorption maximum in the visible spectrum of the former is only slightly displaced to the shorter wavelengths relative to that of the violet absorption of the halogen (518 m$\mu$) in carbon tetrachloride.[7] In general, the lack of a characteristic visible or ultraviolet absorption spectrum in a solution containing an electron donor and an electron acceptor points to the absence of a molecular complex. It must be noted, however, that in dilute solutions the spectra of the products of interaction are the sum of those of the reactants,[8] and that the influence of resonance stabilization must also be considered;[9] solvent perturbation is also of importance.[10] With these reservations in mind spectroscopic data may be used with some confidence as evidence in support of complex formation. Indeed, the literature dealing with molecular complexes is full of references to the use of spectra for the elucidation of compositions and stabilities of molecular complexes. To cite just a few more recent examples, the strong ultraviolet absorption spectrum of iodine in saturated hydrocarbons shows a distinct band around 240 m$\mu$ at $-127°$C and at $25°$C in the presence of a hydrocarbon containing a cyclohexane ring, since this ring has greater donor properties than open-chain saturated hydrocarbons or cyclo-pentane.[11] The same author found considerable absorption in the ultraviolet spectrum when dissolving tetra-nitromethane in cyclohexane; this absorption was absent in the gaseous nitro-compound, while no comparable effect was observed in the case of nitromethane. Spectroscopic data were also used to determine compositions and stabilities of 2:1 and 1:2 molecular complexes formed between 1,3,5-trinitrobenzene or *N*,*N*-dimethylaniline[12] and ethanol; a deep violet or red colour developed in these solutions. Spectral intensity measurements made at 280 m$\mu$ of solutions of nitromethane or 2,2-dinitropropane in primary, secondary or tertiary amines pointed to complex formation;[13] the magnitude of these effects in nitrogenous solvents paralleled the basic strengths of the amines, which in turn could be predicted from inductive effects alone. The absorption maxima of many molecular complexes involving hydrocarbon donors and acid anhydride acceptors have been studied by Chowdhury,[14] while an important review of charge-transfer spectra of complexes formed by neutral molecules was published by G. Briegleb.[15]

Another example concerns the product of interaction between *p*-aminophenyl (donor) and *p*-nitrophenyl (acceptor) aromatic systems.[16] Despite the great differences in the orientation of the rings of the donor and acceptor, there results an intensification of the spectrum and a marked absorption shift to the visible region; this view is supported by Mulliken and Orgel.[17]

The study of the spectra of molecular complexes has also been extended to low-temperature reactions.[11] Thus the fluorescence and absorption spectra of the products of interaction between hexamethylbenzene and chloranil, trinitrobenzoic acid, picryl chloride or nitrobenzene have been studied in dipropylether-isopentane at −190°C; absorption shifts were observed, and were ascribed[18] to charge-transfer during complex formation. In fact the emission fluorescence and absorption spectra were mirror images and corresponded to the same electronic transition, the fluorescence having no relation to the phosphorescence of the hydrocarbons used; the spectral shifts corresponding to the various electron affinities of the acceptors were accompanied by corresponding shifts in the emission bands.

The shift to longer wavelengths consequent upon the formation of molecular complexes has been also observed in the infrared spectrum. Thus in a benzene solution of hydrogen chloride the fundamental absorption of the halide is shifted to longer wavelengths.[19] Similar considerations apply to solutions of aniline in nitrobenzene,[20] of dimethylaniline in s-trinitrobenzene,[21] of methanol or deuterated methanol in benzene,[22] of iodine in pyridine,[23] and of acetyl chloride–titanium tetrachloride, or of propionyl chloride–titanium tetrachloride 1 : 1 complexes;[24] in the last case the C=O frequency is lowered, because the electron acceptor is fixed on the oxygen atom of the C=O group, and the C=O bond order is lowered by 21%. On the other hand, the infrared spectra of occlusion compounds are summations of those of their components, e.g. the product of the reaction between p,p-dinitrobiphenyl with biphenyl.[25] Further, certain features in the spectra of solutions of some metallic ions in mesitylene are due to impurities in the latter.[26]

Infrared absorption and Raman spectra have also been used to study a variety of molecular complexes, though not as extensively as the ultraviolet and visible spectra. The following systems have been investigated: 1 : 1 molecular complexes of iodine–dioxane in inert solvents,[27] organic complexes of ethanol in dilute solution,[28] organic complexes of phenol in dilute solution,[29] organic complexes of pyrrol in dilute solution,[30] and those of chloroform in aqueous solution.[31] The lowering of the infrared frequencies has also been observed in the case of molecular complexes formed between aluminium bromide and nitro-aliphatic or nitro-aromatic compounds in which a bond is formed between the metal and the oxygen of the nitro-group.[32] Similar considerations apply to systems involving ketonic donors, e.g. acetophenone or benzophenone, and certain metallic and metalloidal acceptors, e.g. chlorides of zinc, aluminium, titanium (IV) and ferric iron or boron trifluoride. The C=O frequency is lowered owing to the formation of a metal–carbonyl bond.[33] For instance,[34] the carbonyl frequency of acetone or di-n-propylketone is lowered by 70 cm$^{-1}$ when reacting with boron trifluoride in benzene solution owing to the formation of an oxygen–boron bond (the dipole moment of the di-n-propylketone–boron trifluoride interaction product is 6·59 $D$).

Raman spectra have been applied in the study of the structures of molecular complexes. For instance, the Raman spectrum of aqueous sodium fluoroborate has been analysed in order to determine the bond distance and stretching force constant of the $B-F$ link;[35] the transition from the planar $BF_3$ structure to tetrahedral $BF_4^-$ resulted in a decrease of the force constant in the ratio $4:3$ and an increase of the $B-F$ bond distance from $1\cdot30$ to $1\cdot43$ Å. Results obtained from the Raman spectra of molten $BF_3-HNO_3$ show that the complex is mainly in the ionic form $NO_2^+BF_3OH^-$ while the adduct $(BF_3)_2-HNO_3$ exists as an undissociated molecular complex.[36]

Some interesting observations have been made in the case of solutions of hydrogen halides, carbon monoxide, nitric oxide or methane in non-polar solvents.[37] The infrared absorption spectra of these gaseous solutes display submaxima known as P and R branches. In solution in inert solvents the spectra show "wings" corresponding to the envelopes of the P and R branches of the gaseous state substances, but on either side of the principal band. However, if complex formation occurs between the solutes and a suitable solvent, these "wings" disappear. It is probable that in solution there exists an equilibrium between species retaining free rotation, which is responsible for the P and R branches, and a complex in which free rotation is not allowed. In polar solvents or in the case of association of the solute the complex species predominates, the "wings" disappear, and a central absorption maximum indicative of complex formation makes its appearance at a frequency lower than the fundamental one characteristic of the species in the gaseous state. This hypothesis has been checked with respect to hydrogen bromide in carbon disulphide by predicting that a variation in temperature should move the "wings" towards the central maximum; this was found to occur in the range $-75°$ to $25°C$.

**The compositions** of the molecular complexes may be studied by a variety of spectroscopic methods. One of the earliest attempts to determine the composition of molecular complexes was made by Priest and Schumb[38] in course of an investigation of solutions of benzene and tungsten hexafluoride in carbon tetrachloride. The optical densities of the solutions of these compounds in the spectral range 520–570 m$\mu$ were found to vary directly with the concentration of either component so that the formula $C_6H_6WF_6$ was assigned to the red complex. In certain cases it is possible to identify both the complex and one of the reactants by investigating the isobiestic point. For example, the reaction between iodine and dimethylacetamide in carbon tetrachloride[39] gives rise to molecular complex formation involving the oxygen of the amide. The existence of the isobiestic point† indicates the presence of two species in solution, viz. the complex and the free amide; the presence of the complex is inferred from the shift of the carbonyl absorption in the infrared region, since there is generally a lowering of the $C=O$ interaction frequency on complex formation, as noted previously.

Another spectroscopic method applicable to solid molecular complexes[40] is based on the ratio of the optical densities at two wavelengths. Thus, if one component has a maximum optical density $D_1$ at $\lambda_1$ and $D_2$ at $\lambda_2$ then for very dilute solution $D_1/D_2 = a$ is the same before and after the precipitation of the complex provided that the complex is of the $1:1$ type, e.g. benzoquinone–phenol in hexane, or benzidine–$m$-dinitrobenzene in ethanol. An important procedure is the method of continuous variation[41] and its modifications[42] which have been used to determine compositions and stabilities of molecular complexes, e.g. maleic acid-substituted styrenes in chloroform solutions.[43] This method makes use of any measurable additive property, provided that this property has different values for the various species present in the solution of the reactants. The plot of the additive property, e.g. optical density, versus composition of the solution is a curve with a maximum corresponding to the formula of the product.

The spectrophotometric method was also used to determine stability constants of complexes in solution. The earliest attempt was that by Michaelis and Granick[1] who evaluated the relative stabilities of the products of interaction between quinones and certain phenolic compounds or hexamethylbenzene in various

---

†The term isobiestic point (point of equal extinction) applies to any wavelength where the optical densities are the same for two solutions of a substance capable of existing in two forms. The occurrence of an isobiestic point indicates the existence of two substances in solution (see ref. 42, Rose, p. 245)

solvents. The equilibrium constant for a 1:1 complex is given by the relation

$$(3.1) \qquad k = \frac{[X]}{[A-X][D-X]},$$

where the square brackets denote concentrations (moles per litre), and $X$, $A$ and $D$ refer to the complex, acceptor and donor, respectively. Since the equilibrium concentration $[X]$ of the complex is generally small compared to those of the reactants, therefore $[A-X] \approx [X]$ and $[D-X] \approx [X]$, so that

$$(3.2) \qquad k \approx \frac{[X]}{[A][D]}.$$

On the other hand, the Beer–Lambert law leads to the relation

$$(3.3) \qquad d = \epsilon l c,$$

where $c$ is the concentration of the species in moles per litre, $d$ is the optical density of the solution of the complex $X$, $\epsilon$ is the molar extinction coefficient, and $l$ is the path length, i.e. the thickness of the absorption cell in centimetres. It follows that for solutions in 1 cm absorption cells

$$(3.4) \qquad k \cdot \epsilon \approx \frac{d}{[A][D]}.$$

The values of $k\epsilon$ may be taken as representing stabilities of the complex, provided that the extinction coefficients for all the complexes studied are closely similar. This procedure has been used for evaluating stability constants of complexes formed by s-trinitrobenzene with aromatic amines,[44] and by various aromatic compounds with tetranitromethane.[45] The above procedures are, however, inaccurate, for the values of $\epsilon$ for even closely related complexes are not equal, and eqn. (3.4) is quite inaccurate in many cases.

The study of the ultraviolet spectra (at 290 m$\mu$) of iodine and benzene in carbon tetrachloride led to the development of a more accurate method for determining stability constants and extinction coefficients of complexes.[6] This method is based on two assumptions: firstly, it is assumed that an appreciable fraction of the iodine in solution exists in the form of one type of a

1 : 1 complex with benzene; secondly, the absorptions of the reactants are negligible in the spectral region under study. It is worth stating that the presence of only one type of 1 : 1 complex can be inferred from the constancy of the molar absorption coefficient during temperature $T$ changes, or from the linearity between the stability constant and $1/T$ in a narrow temperature range.[46] In the presence of a large excess of benzene the optical density $d$ at 290 m$\mu$ is related to the equilibrium constant $k$ by the Benesi–Hildebrand equation.[6]

$$(3.5) \qquad \frac{l[A]}{d} = \frac{1}{\epsilon k} \times \frac{1}{X_D} + \frac{1}{\epsilon},$$

where the symbols are the same as in eqn. (3.4) and $X_D$ is the mole fraction of the donor benzene species; the optical density relates to the charge-transfer $(E \leftarrow N)$ band. The values of $k$ and $\epsilon$ can be found by plotting the left-hand side of eqn. (3.5) versus the reciprocals of the corresponding mole fractions of benzene in the solvent and calculating the slope $(1/k\epsilon)$ and intercept $(1/\epsilon)$ of the straight line obtained. This method has been used to determine equilibrium constants for a number of complexes e.g. aluminium bromide,[47] sulphur dioxide,[48] chlorine,[49] iodine monochloride,[50] oxalyl chloride,[51] quinones or maleic anhydride[52] in aromatic solvents, of the acridine–acridinium perchlorate complex in dichloromethane[53] and of the indole–tetracyanoethylene complex in dichloromethane.[187]

The stability constants of addition complexes of aromatic hydrocarbons and amines with aromatic nitro-compounds in chloroform solution have been studied by a modified Benesi–Hildebrand procedure.[54] Both the original and the modified methods suffer, however, from several disadvantages. Firstly, no account is taken of the contribution of the free acceptor to the observed optical density. Moreover, the values of the molar extinction coefficients and stability constants do change with the varying donor solvent ratio owing to a slight shift of the peak of maximum absorption. Finally, the observed values of the intercept $(1/\epsilon)$ are very small so that the accuracy of the $\epsilon$-values obtained from them is unsatisfactory. In very dilute solutions the error involved owing to the absorption shift is very small,[50, 55] so that a suitable correction for the optical contribution of the free acceptor species renders the method more accurate.[56]

In order to eliminate the effect of superimposed absorption of iodine, Nagakura[57] used the following equation for determination of the stability constant of the complex of iodine with triethylamine

$$(3.6) \qquad k_c = \frac{[C_D(k_0 - k') + C_D'(k - k_0)]}{[C_D C_D'(k' - k)]},$$

where $k_0$, $k$ and $k'$ are absorbances at a fixed wavelength of solutions containing the same concentration of the halogen but different concentrations of the amine, viz. 0, $C_D$ and $C_D'$, respectively.

Another procedure[58] consists of plotting the values of $(lX_1[A]/d)$ versus $X_D$. This has the following advantages: the initial slope at very low concentrations can be determined, since one extrapolates through regions of decreasing concentrations to the intercept. Moreover, in the absence of a straight line, this procedure reduces the errors involved in measurements. It is also necessary to consider the deviations of solutions from ideal behaviour. Thus the plots of $(lX_D[A]/d)$ against $X_D$, or of $(l[A][D]/d)$ against $[D]$ differ to a considerable extent, and the resulting equilibrium constants do not obey the thermodynamic relationship,

$$(3.7) \qquad K_c = K_x \cdot V_s,$$

where $V_s$ is the molar volume of the solvent, and $K_c$ and $K_x$ are the thermodynamic equilibrium constant in terms of concentration or mole fractions, respectively. Hence the reported values of equilibrium constants $k$ and extinction coefficients $\epsilon$ obtained by the Benesi–Hildebrand method are subject to some uncertainty, though in certain cases the product $k\epsilon$ is constant for a wide range of concentrations.[59]

The problem of solutions containing several molecular complexes at once is more difficult. In this case it is necessary to consider the effect of the presence of the complexes on the determination of the equilibrium constant for the formation of a given complex. For instance, 1,3,5-trinitrobenzene $(T)$

reacts with $N,N$-dimethylaniline $(A)$ to form $1:1$, $1:2$ and $2:1$ complexes[12] in chloroform solution. Thus, in the presence of a large excess of the amine the method consists of plotting $y = A_0 T_0 / d_c (A_0 + T_0)$ versus $x = 1/(A_0 + T_0)$, where $A_0$ and $T_0$ represent the initial concentration of the amine and hydrocarbon respectively, and $d_c = d_t - A_0 \epsilon_A - T_0 \epsilon_T$, where $d_t$ is the total optical density of the solution of the complex, and $\epsilon_A$ and $\epsilon_T$ are the extinction coefficients of the pure reactants $A$ and $T$, respectively, at the same wavelength. The intercept of the straight lines obtained is equal to $1/\epsilon$, and the slope is equal to $1/k\epsilon$, where $k$ is the equilibrium constant (litres per mole) and $\epsilon$ is the extinction coefficient relating to the complex. At 440 m$\mu$ the respective values of $k$ and $\epsilon$ are 0·83 and 1130 at 24·8°C. A correction has, however, been introduced, since it is necessary to plot

$$\frac{A_0 T_0}{d_c (A_0 + T_0 - TA)} \quad \text{against} \quad \frac{1}{A_0 + T_0 - TA},$$

where $TA$ is the concentration of the complex. In practice, the value of $k$ obtained by the approximate method is used to calculate $TA$ and then to correct the data of $\epsilon$ and $k$ previously obtained. For other ratios of amine and hydrocarbon in the presence of other complexes modifications of the above are essential. In fact, these authors have explored the effect of the $T_1 A_2$ and $T_2 A_1$ complexes on the determination of the equilibrium constant of $TA$ by adapting their original equation and using suitable values for $d_c$.

There are two other important objections to the Benesi–Hildebrand treatment. Firstly, in weak complexes,[188] where there is no need to invoke the Mulliken–Orgel theory of "contact" and "complex" spectra, the Benesi–Hildebrand plot over-estimates the value of $\epsilon$ and underestimates that of the stability constant $k$. If these are revaluated, then a correlation may be obtained between $\epsilon$ and $k$ for families of related complexes.

Secondly, the criterion that the linearity of the plot indicates the presence of only stable $1:1$ charge transfer complexes and/or contact absorption has been recently challenged by Johnson and Bowen,[189] as a result of investigations concerning a number of 1:1, 1:2 and 2:1 complexes. It was also found that the value of the stability constant $k$ obtained by the Benesi–Hildebrand procedure varies systematically with wavelength, e.g. for the tetracyanoethylene–naphthalene complex in carbon tetrachloride. At least two complexes of different stoichiometries appear to exist in this case. The study of the relation between $k$ and wavelength is claimed to give information about multiple equilibria, i.e. existence of complexes of different stoichiometries.

As noted before, one of the assumptions governing the validity of the Benesi–Hildebrand equilibrium is the presence in solution of one type of a 1:1 complex. If there are several types of 1:1 complexes of the two components in solution, then the equilibrium constant measures the whole of the complexing, whereas the extinction coefficient is given by a weight-average value, since the various types of the complexes may not absorb at all the wavelengths at which the Benesi–Hildebrand equilibrium applies.[17] Hence in ideal solutions $K$ would be the total equilibrium constant and thermodynamically correct, so that various methods for evaluating the constant should give the same value. For instance, the equilibrium constants of naphthalene picrates determined by the partition and spectroscopic methods are very nearly the same,[60] though it should be noted that they vary with concentration owing to the non-ideality of the solution, and there is a concentration-dependent change of the spectra of the moieties. Similar considerations apply to the benzene–iodine complex.[61] There is, however, a general lack of accuracy when using the Benesi–Hildebrand procedure, because contactual interactions beteween the components may cause absorption in the relevant spectral region. Hence the Benesi–Hildebrand plot may still be linear since the concentrations of such "contact species" may vary linearly with $1/X_D$. On the other hand, the values of the extinction coefficient will tend to become more and more excessive at lower concentrations, until at infinite dilution the extinction coefficient will tend towards infinity, i.e. the straight line will pass through the origin.[17]

A more rigorous treatment involving a spectrophotometric evaluation of equilibrium constants of molecular complexes has been given by Rose and Drago,[62] who have eliminated some of the assumptions underlying the Benesi–Hildebrand and the

Ketelaar methods; the latter[56] applies to cases involving over-lapping bands. The Rose–Drago equation may be written in the form

$$(3.8) \qquad k^{-1} = \frac{A - A^\circ}{\epsilon_C - \epsilon_I} - C_I - C_D + \frac{C_D C_I (\epsilon_C - \epsilon_I)}{A - A^\circ},$$

where $k$ is the equilibrium constant, $A^\circ$ is the absorbance of the initial concentration of the iodine acceptor, $C_D$ is that of the base (donor), $C_I$ is that of the iodine acceptor, $\epsilon_I$ is the molar extinction coefficient of iodine, $\epsilon_C$ that of the complex, and $A$ is the total absorbance at any given wavelength for a 1 cm cell. The above equation contains two unknowns, $k$ and $\epsilon_C$, so that it is necessary to construct two simultaneous equations from pairs of data.[57,62 63] This equation has been used to study the benzene-iodine system in carbon tetrachloride, the trimethylamine–iodine, biphenyl–iodine, dioxane–iodine and hexaethylbenzene–iodine interactions. It is claimed that this equation is superior to the Benesi–Hildebrand relation, since it does not assume the comple-tion of the donor–acceptor reaction and it caters for nearly all cases, such as band overlap or where the extinction coefficient of the complex is a constant independent of the base concentration and the bulk dielectric constant of the solvent. Equations for stoichiometry other than 1 : 1 can be derived and applied with success. In addition, the equation gives the Benesi–Hildebrand and Ketelaar equations as special cases.

While the majority of spectrophotometric methods for deter-mining stability constants of molecular complexes have been confined to the use of spectral data in the ultraviolet and visible ranges, attempts have been made to extend this treatment to infrared and Raman spectra. Thus Popov *et al.*[64] determined the stability constants of the molecular complexes boron–iodine monochloride, dioxane–iodine cyanide, metrazole–iodine cyanide and pyridine–ICN, the corresponding formation constants being 0·7, 1·2, 15 and 51 in fair agreement with the results obtained by means of ultraviolet spectra of these substances [50,65] Fuson[29,30] determined the stability constant of the products of interaction between phenol or pyrrole, as donors, and chlorobenzene, ben-zene, pyridine or hexamethylbenzene as acceptors by examining the values of the vibration frequencies of the OH and NH bands in their free and associated state. He found a linear relationship between the constant and the frequency displacement associated with complex formation. In the absence of complex formation, as, for example, in solutions of the donors in carbon tetrachloride, no frequency displacement occurred. This displacement increased with the increasing basicity of the solvent, the only exception being pyridine.

Another application of infrared and Raman spectra is in the realm of ionization. For instance, the mode of ionization of gallium dihalides was elucidated without difficulty by Raman spectra, since the anion $[GaX_4]^-$ is the only polyatomic species present in the molten complex. The Raman spectrum of the fused $GaCl_3$–$POCl_3$ adduct has been interpreted in terms of the covalent complex $Cl_3PO \rightarrow GaCl_3$, though a small concentration of free ions, such as $GaCl_4^-$ and $POCl_2^+$ is also present.[66] It is worth noting than an unambiguous conclusion is only possible if the extent of ionization does not exceed about 1%.

The application of infrared and Raman methods for evaluating stability constants presents considerable difficulties. Firstly, these spectra are less convenient experimentally[64] than the ultraviolet and visible spectra, since many solvents absorb greatly at the longer wavelengths, so that concentrated solutions have to be used; this leads to gross variations in the values of activity coefficients and thus of those of the classical stability constants.[31] In addition, one can hardly use aqueous solutions in the infrared region, and the experimental treatment is rather difficult.[67]

## General remarks

Since donor–acceptor interaction implies a certain amount of charge-transfer in the ground state of the complex, it follows that an electron is partially removed from a bonding orbital of the donor to an antibonding orbital of the acceptor. As a result, there is a decrease of bond order for at least one bond in each moiety and the following three phenomena will occur:

(i) A decrease in the vibrational frequencies of those modes whose force constants are sensitive to active orbitals involved in the interaction; the more localized the active orbital or the smaller the complex, the greater the decrease of the frequencies.

(ii) An increase in some bond lengths of the moieties.

(iii) Appearance of some vibrational modes, otherwise absent because of symmetry forbiddenness in the isolated moieties, in the spectrum of the molecular complexes; this is due to a decrease in total symmetry usually following complex formation.

These phenomena have been observed in many cases.[46, 68]

The use of the spectral data has been extended to thermodynamic studies of molecular complex formation. The literature on this topic is very extensive, but a few of the more recent examples will suffice to show the scope of this technique.

Twenty-three π-complexes of tetracyanoethylene with aromatic hydrocarbons in dichloromethane solvent have been examined by spectrophotometric procedures in order to determine thermodynamic data,[69] while the strong 1:1 complex formed by tetracyanoethylene with dimethylsulphoxide was studied by spectrophotometric and electron paramagnetic resonance methods;[186] the iodine–aromatic hydrocarbons complexes have been extensively studied in this connection,[51, 62, 70] while the thermodynamics of complex formation between Lewis acids and amines have been investigated by Wenz,[71] and those of the system iodine–ethanol and iodine–aliphatic amines by Amako and Yada, respectively.[72]

## 2. Colligative methods

These methods are concerned with the application of data derived from the study of freezing or melting points and of vapour pressures of multicomponent systems. The use of freezing point data is based on the observation that complex formation is associated with the existence of two or more eutectic mixtures, and that maxima in melting point–composition diagrams correspond to the composition of complexes.[73] Cryoscopy has even been used to determine thermodynamic stability constants of 1:1 complexes in organic solvents.

In some cases the molecular complex has a relatively high

lattice free-energy as compared to that of the solid solute, so that it has an incongruent melting point, e.g. the solid aluminium bromide–benzene complex[74] displays this feature at 37°C.

Thermal analysis has been extensively used to study interactions between boron trifluoride and a variety of donors,[75] hydrogen halides and $\pi$-orbital donors[76] and those between aromatic compounds and metallic halides.[76,77] As regards the hydrogen halides, thermal analysis showed that hydrogen chloride formed 1:1 and 2:1 complexes with alkenes, and 1:1, 1:2 and 1:4 complexes with alkynes, while no complex formation occurred with saturated hydrocarbons. In each case the $\pi$-orbitals of the alkenes and alkynes are involved; for the 1:2 alkenes and 1:4 alkynes each $\pi$-orbital accumulates two electrons, and a weak hydrogen bond is formed between the halide and the $\pi$-orbital donor. Similar considerations apply to the interaction between hydrogen chloride and benzene, methyl–benzenes, anthracene or *trans*-stilbene, while no molecular complexes are formed with cyclo-hexane or cyclo-propane.[76] The existence of two complexes is demonstrated by the appearance of two distinct liquidus curves, e.g. interaction between organic donors and nitrogen oxides (C. C. Addison and J. C. Sheldon, ref. 77). In many cases the course of direction of the liquidus curve of a common component in a binary system may throw light on the composition of the complex. For instance, phase rule study of the liquidus curves of the systems[78] $SbCl_3$–$C_6H_5CH_2OH$, $SbCl_3$–$C_6H_5I$, $SbBr_3$–$C_{10}N_8$, $SbBr_3$–triphenyl methane, $NaF$–$CdF_2$ and $NaF$–$Na_2SO_4$ show that the compositions correspond to 1:1, 1:1, 2:1, 2:1, 1:1 and 1:1 ratios, respectively. It must be noted, however, that the literature abounds in disagreements concerning the existence and composition of molecular complexes inferred from thermal analysis data. There is, for instance, a conflict of opinion about the products of interaction between sulphur dioxide and benzene, toluene, ethylbenzene or tetralin.[79] It is also recognized that in certain cases the thermal method cannot indicate the existence of complexes, e.g. that formed between benzene and chloroform,[80] while many technical difficulties render this method somewhat inaccurate.[81] For example, the preparation of solidification curves is rendered difficult because of secondary reactions, supercooling and occurrence of solidification blanks. Some improvements may be effected in the case of systems melting above room temperature by using hot-stage microscopes and observing the formation of the complex at the boundary between the molten reactants. It is claimed that this technique has been successfully applied to the study of 1:1 complexes, e.g. s-trinitrobenzene–β-naphthyl-amine, phenanthrene–2,4-dinitrophenol, naphthalene–2,4-dinitro-toluene, and others.[81, 82] Another source of inaccuracy is the tacit assumption that the surface tensions of the "complex" solutes do not depend on the concentrations of any other solutes present in the solutions.

Despite the extensive applications of thermal analysis to the study of complexes in general, very few attempts have been made to measure stability constants by the melting point–composition method. In congruent type diagrams (two eutectics and a maximum corresponding to a complex) the degree of dissociation of the complex in the fused state is assumed to be indicated by the flattening of the melting point–composition curves at the distectic point, provided that the complex is moderately stable, e.g. antimony trichloride–methylbenzene systems (T. Sinomiya, ref. 77). Sinomiya (loc. cit.) estimated the relative stabilities of a number of complexes derived from inorganic and organic compounds by considering an empirical factor $\tau$, "the melting point elevation", defined by the equation

$$(3.9) \qquad \tau = t_C - \frac{mt_A + nt_B}{m + n},$$

where $m/n$ is the mole ratio of the two moieties in the complex, and $t_A$, $t_B$ and $t_C$ refer to the melting points of the two components $A$ and $B$ and the complex, respectively. It must be noted, however, that the factor $\tau$ can only serve as a qualitative guide for the study of relative stabilities, since it has no theoretical foundation and merely represents the difference between the melting point of the complex and the weighted mean of the melting points of the moieties making up the complex. Despite these difficulties this procedure has been found to be useful in the study of complexes of naphthylamines with substituted nitrobenzenes, and of alkylbenzenes with antimony trichloride.

The thermal analysis method has been used for evaluating various thermodynamic quantities. Thus, entropies (per mole) of fusion of molecular complexes have been found from binary solid–liquid phase diagrams, e.g. urea–phenol ($\Delta S_f$ of the $AB_2$ complex = 22·7 e.u.), picric acid–naphthalene ($\Delta S_f$ of $AB$ = 19·9 e.u.) and benzophenone–diphenylamine ($\Delta S_f$ of $AB$ = 19·3 e.u.) (R. P. Rastogi and R. K. Nigam, ref. 77). Energies of interactions can be also evaluated from pressure–composition phase diagrams, e.g. phosphorus trichloride–trimethylamine solid complex at −46·5°C (R. R. Holmes, ref. 77).

Vapour-pressure methods can also be used for the quantitative study of molecular complexes. For instance, the partial pressure of hydrogen chloride or bromide over their solution in benzene or of hexamethylbenzene in carbon tetrachloride shows negative deviations from ideal behaviour, i.e. from Raoult's law, although it obeys Henry's law.[83] These deviations may be due, however, to a number of causes in addition to complex formation. For example, vapour-pressure studies appear to show that for solutions of hydrogen chloride in benzene or nitrobenzene the latter solvent is a stronger base than benzene; this, however, is contrary to recent views. It is also recognized that positive deviations from Raoult's law in the case of cyclohexanol, phenol and cresol solutions of hydrogen chloride do not point to complex formation,[84] as originally supposed. On the other hand, this method has been successfully used to study the molecular complexes formed by the aluminium chloride–hydrogen chloride system with toluene,[85] and of chloroform–dioxan mixtures.[86] It appears that one mole of hydrogen chloride is absorbed for each mole of aluminium chloride in a toluene solution at −84·1°C, and a green solution is obtained. At −45·4°C, however, a yellow solution is produced which corresponds to the absorption of one mole of hydrogen chloride per two moles of the metallic halide (in each case one dissolves the metal halide in a prepared solution of hydrogen chloride in toluene). The postulated complexes are thus $CH_3C_6H_6{}^+AlCl_4{}^-$ and $CH_3C_6H_6{}^+\text{-}Al_2Cl_7{}^-$ for the green and yellow solutions, respectively. Although toluene and aluminium chloride do not interact at −84·1°C, benzene and aluminium bromide[87] give a solid (1:1) complex at 15°C of composition $Al_2Br_6 \cdot 2C_6H_6$. There are some indications that aluminium bromide–*m*-xylene or bromine–mesitylene complexes also exist.[88]

An extension of O'Brien's work (ref. 83) is the vapour pressure method as modified by Brown and Brady,[89] who investigated solutions of aromatic hydrocarbons and hydrogen chloride in toluene or *n*-heptane. They measured the vapour pressures of the halide at low temperatures (*ca.* −78·5°C) in order to render negligible the partial vapour pressure of the hydrocarbons; the use of dilute solutions of the hydrocarbons reduced the effect of secondary interactions on the vapour pressure of hydrogen chloride. The equilibrium constant for complex formation was evaluated by using Henry's law, viz:

$$(3.10) \qquad p_{HCl} = c \cdot x_{HCl},$$

where $p_{HCl}$ is the measured vapour pressure of hydrogen chloride, and $x_{HCl}$ is its mole fraction in solution; $c$ is the constant of Henry's law which decreases with increasing concentrations of the aromatic hydrocarbons. The formation constant of the complex $DA$, where $D$ is the donor hydrocarbons and $A$ is the acceptor halide, is given by the relation

$$(3.11) \qquad k = \frac{x_X}{x_D \cdot p_A},$$

where $p_A = p_{HCl}$, and $x_X$ and $x_D$ represent the mole fractions of the complex and aromatic hydrocarbon, respectively. The term $x_X$ can be found from the differences in the known mole fraction of hydrogen chloride in solution ($x_{HCl}$) and that of the halide in the pure solvent; the value of $x_D$ ($D$ = aromatic hydrocarbon) is taken as the difference between the mole fraction of the total aromatic hydrocarbon in solution and that of the molecular complex. In general the values of the equilibrium constants have been found to increase with decreasing concentration of the aromatic hydrocarbons. It is, of course, assumed that the products of interaction are 1:1 complexes and that the laws of dilute solutions are obeyed. The latter assumption is, however, open to serious objections, so that the relative basicities of the hydrocarbons cannot be accurately represented by the equilibrium constant. A much more realistic criterion of these properties of aromatic hydrocarbons is the series of single-stage separation factors in distribution studies (see below). On the other hand, the values of the equilibrium constants serve as a qualitative guide for establishing the tendency of the various hydrocarbons to donate electrons to suitable acceptors. In this connection, the hydrogen fluoride–boron fluoride complexes of *m*-xylene and mesitylene,[90] aluminium chloride–hydrogen chloride complexes of toluene,[85] and the corresponding molecular complexes of aluminium bromide[87] and others have been studied by the vapour pressure method. For example, mesitylene reduces the vapour pressure of a boron trifluoride solution in hydrogen fluoride until the mole ratio of the boron trifluoride to mesitylene is nearly unity; only then does the vapour pressure of the solution begin to increase. A similar situation arises in $BF_3$–HF solutions in the presence of *m*-xylene, though the vapour pressure of the solutions increases significantly with increasing boron trifluoride concentration well before the boron trifluoride–*m*-xylene ratio reaches unity. In other words, the *m*-xylene complex appears to be much less stable than that of mesitylene.

### 3. Solubility method

Solubility measurements have been used to some extent to identify donor–acceptor complexes and determine their stability constants. The earliest attempts to use this procedure were made at the end of the nineteenth century[91] in connection with picric acid complexes. More recent work is concerned with a large variety of substances. For instance, a number of complexes of hydrogen chloride with aromatic compounds have been found to be soluble in anhydrous liquid hydrogen fluoride, while alkanes and cyclo-alkanes are nearly insoluble in the same medium.[89, 92] The process of dissolution can probably be represented by the equation

$$C_6H_6 + HF \rightleftharpoons C_6H_6H^+ + F^-.$$

It should be noted, however, that direct comparison of the relative solubilities of the aromatic hydrocarbons, even in a common solvent, cannot represent the scale of relative strengths of these substances unless the experimental data are first corrected to the same vapour pressure of the aromatic compound.[93] For example, benzene is more soluble in liquid hydrogen fluoride at 0° C than naphthalene on an absolute scale; after considering the vapour-pressure variations of these aromatic hydrocarbons, it is found that naphthalene is about eight times more soluble in the fluoride solvent than benzene.

Solutions of iodine in complexing solvents, such as fluorobenzene or ethyl iodide, and in non-complexing solvents, such as 1,2-dibromoethane or perfluoroheptane, were investigated over a wide range of concentrations[89] (Hildebrand and Scott; Jepson and Rowlinson). In order to make valid comparisons between these solutions in overlapping concentration ranges, it is necessary to correct for the energy of vaporization per unit volume of solvent. It is found that the experimental solubility of iodine in complexing solvents is greater than that in inert or non-complexing solvents. Furthermore, the plots of log $N_2$, where $N_2$ is the mole fraction of the solute, versus the reciprocal of the absolute temperature do not give a family of curves, i.e. curves with similar slopes, as do solutions of iodine in inert solvents. Moreover, while the plots of $(\partial \log N_2 / \partial \log T)_{\text{satd.}}$ versus $-\log N_2$ for the latter solutions give one straight line (see ref. 89, Hildebrand and Glew), the corresponding curves for solutions of molecular complexes lie below that straight line; also, the solubility of the halogen in complexing solvents is greater than that calculated from the Hildebrand equation applicable to regular solutions, i.e. those, for which the curves derived by plotting log $N_2$ against $1/T$ can be accommodated by a single straight line. Iodine in inert, non-complexing solvents, such as carbon tetrachloride or aliphatic hydrocarbons, gives rise to regular solutions.

Complex formation constants have been determined by means of solubility studies, although this procedure is open to serious objections owing to various assumptions on which the calculations are based. Thus the interaction between picric acid and stilbene or related compounds, such as $p$-chloro- and $p$-methyl-stilbene in chloroform solution[91, 94] is assumed to yield a 1:1 complex, the solution of which is intensely coloured. It is further assumed that the equilibrium (free) concentration $[P]_E$ of the acid solution is equal to its solubility in pure chloroform, while the corresponding concentration of the complex $[X]_E$ is related to the *total* concentrations of the acid $[P]_T$ and aromatic hydrocarbon $[S]_T$ by the expressions

$$[P]_T = [P]_E + [X]_E$$

and

$$[S]_T = [S]_E + [X]_E,$$

where $[S]_E$ is the equilibrium (free) concentration of the aromatic hydrocarbon solution.

Another assumption is that the concentration of the free aromatic compound in aqueous solution at a fixed ionic strength—made up by means of potassium nitrate—is not affected by replacing the potassium ions by slower ions. On introducing these approximations, it is possible to calculate the equilibrium constant by means of the relation

(3.12)
$$k = \frac{[X]_E}{[S]_E [P]_E}.$$

For instance, the equilibrium constant for the interactions between picric acid and stilbene leads to a nearly constant value of about 0·9 for stilbene concentrations ranging between 0·05 M and 0·16 M. Similar procedures with their attendant limitations have been used for investigating the equilibria between picric acid and ethyl cinnamate, and s-trinitrobenzene with various aromatic amines in chloroform solutions.[91, 95]

The formation constants of certain 1:1 molecular complexes have been determined by the solubility method, using Kortüm's equation[89]

$$K_N = \frac{N_S - N_0}{N_0(N_D - N_S + N_0)}$$

where $K_N$ is the equilibrium constant of complex formation expressed in terms of mole fraction, $N_D$ is the mole fraction of the donor, while $N_S$ and $N_0$ are the mole fractions of the acceptor (in this case iodine) and the complexing and non-complexing solvents, respectively. The method consists of measuring the solubility of the halogen in a non-complexing solvent in the presence and absence of the donor. However, there are some limitations here, since the nature of the solvent affects the values of $K_N$ owing to the change of the ratio of the activity coefficients in the thermodynamic equation for the reaction $(D + A \rightleftharpoons DA)$. Though it is found in practice that $K_N$ values of the Kortüm equation, which is not a strict thermodynamic relation, remain constant for a number of donors, it would be necessary to use the thermodynamic equation, which includes the relevant activity coefficients; the latter vary, of course, with the nature of the solvent, hence $K_N$ varies as well under similar conditions.

A somewhat modified technique has been used for investigating the effect of silver ions on the solutilities of aromatic compounds in aqueous solutions at a constant ionic strength.[96] It appears from the abnormal increase in solubility of the aromatic compounds in presence of increasing amounts of silver ions that $1:1$ and $2:1$ molecular complexes probably exist, viz.

$$(3.13) \qquad Ag^+ + D \rightleftharpoons AgD^+; \; k_1 = \frac{[Ag \cdot D^+]}{[Ag^+][D]}$$

and

$$(3.14) \qquad Ag^+ + Ag \cdot D^+ \rightleftharpoons Ag_2 \cdot D^{2+}; \; k_2 = \frac{[Ag_2 \cdot D^{2+}]}{[Ag^+][Ag \cdot D^+]},$$

where $D$ is the aromatic compound. The values of the stability constant $k$ were calculated by means of the equation

$$(3.15) \qquad k = [D]_C / \{[Ag^+]_T - [D]_C - [Ag_2 \cdot D^{2+}]\}[D]_E,$$

where the subscripts $C$, $T$ and $E$ refer to the complex $(Ag \cdot D^+)$, total (free and complexed silver ion) and free aromatic equilibrium concentrations, respectively. By neglecting the very small term $[Ag_2 \cdot D^{2+}]$ and evaluating the term $[D]$ from solubility measurements of saturated solution of the aromatic hydrocarbons $(D)$ in $1N$ potassium nitrate solution and $[D]_C$ from the measured solubility of $D$ in the silver-ion solution, the value of $k$ can be found. It is also seen from eqns. (3.13) and (3.14) that

$$(3.16) \qquad k = k_1 + k_2[Ag^+]_T$$

so that a plot of $k$ versus $[Ag^+]_T$ should give a straight line of slope $k_2$ and intercept $k_1$. This method has been applied to a large number of substances in silver nitrate or silver perchlorate aqueous solutions, and evidence[65] has been obtained pointing to the existence of the species $Ag_2 \cdot D^{2+}$.

## 4. Distribution method

This procedure has been of some importance in connection with the evaluation of the relative electron-donor capacities of aromatic compounds[90, 97] and equilibrium constants of formation of molecular complexes. Among the systems studied by this method are the following: complexes of silver ions with aromatic amines (1 : 1 and 1 : 2) in a cyclohexane–water partition medium;[98] products of interaction between silver ions and olefins;[99] or cresol;[100] complexes of picric acid with aromatic hydrocarbons, aniline and nitro-aromatic compounds in chloroform solution;[97] those of boron trifluoride with aromatic hydrocarbons.[90]

The distribution method is based either on the determination of single-stage separation factors or on the effect of electron donors on the distribution of an electron acceptor in a medium of two immiscible solvents. The former procedure is used for comparing the ability of various aromatic hydrocarbons to interact with an electron acceptor. Thus, in the case of two aromatic substances, 1 and 2, the single-stage separation factor $\alpha$ is given by the relation

$$(3.17) \qquad \alpha_{2,1} = \frac{x_2 \cdot x_2'}{x_1 \cdot x_1'},$$

where $x_1$ and $x_2$ are the mole fractions of the hydrocarbons in the extract phase; those primed refer to the raffinate. For example, solutions of hexamethylbenzene or toluene (compound 2) in $n$-heptane containing $p$-xylene (compound 1) are subjected to batchwise extraction at room temperature with hydrogen fluoride containing 0·5 mole of boron trifluoride per mole of aromatic material in the system. The separation factor $\alpha$ can then be obtained by analysing the hydrogen fluoride and $n$-heptane phases at equilibrium. It was found that the $\alpha$-values for hexamethylbenzene and toluene were 44,500 and 0·01, respectively, the reaction being

$$D + HF + BF_3 \rightleftharpoons DH^+BF_4^-,$$

where $D$ is the donor aromatic hydrocarbon. It must be noted that, in general, the capacity of the $BF_3$–HF system for complexing with aromatic hydrocarbons is sensitive to the presence of substituents on the aromatic nucleus, so that it is possible to develop a method for separating mixtures of various alkylbenzenes, as well as of their isomers.

The second method has been used for evaluating equilibrium constants of complex formation. For instance, the partition[97] of picric acid between chloroform and water is affected by the presence of varying amounts of aromatic substances in the organic phase owing to the formation of a picric acid–aromatic complex in the chloroform layer. Let the increase of the concentration of the acid in the organic layer be $(a - n)$, where $n$ and $a$ are the normal and increased values, respectively; this increase due to complex formation in the chloroform layer is, however, opposed by the salting-out effect of the unreacted aromatic hydrocarbon (donor), which tends to lower the acid concentration in the non-aqueous phase from say $a$ to $b$. It follows that the total molar acid concentration $T$ in chloroform at equilibrium is given by

(3.18)
$$T = a + b - n.$$

The equilibrium constant $k$ for the formation of a 1 : 1 complex is given by

(3.19)
$$k = \frac{a - n}{n[X - (a - n)]}$$

where $X$ is the concentration of the aromatic compound in the chloroform layer $[X \gg (a - n)]$. In addition, the constant $k_1$ for the depression of the solubility of picric acid in chloroform solution by the aromatic compounds is given by the equation

$$(3.20) \qquad k_1 = \frac{n - b}{yX}$$

while the apparent solubility constant $k_2$ is represented by

$$(3.21) \qquad k_2 = \frac{X - n}{nX}.$$

These constants are approximately related by the expression

$$(3.22) \qquad k = k_1 + k_2.$$

The term $n$ can be evaluated from the picric-acid concentration in the aqueous phase, using the known partition coefficient of the acid between water and chloroform; $T$ can be determined by analysis of the chloroform phase at equilibrium, while $X$ is chosen so that it is large compared to $(a - n)$. Since it is known from experiments on the effect of non-aromatic hydrocarbons, e.g. hexane or decalin, on the distribution of picric acid between water and chloroform that the salting-out coefficient $k_1$ is equal to $0 \cdot 0038V$, where $V$ is the molecular volume of the hydrocarbon, and $k_2$ can be calculated from eqn. (3.21) it follows that $k$ may be found. This method does not, however, take into consideration the phenomenon of self-association of picric acid in chloroform solution, nor the interaction of the acid with the organic solvent. Furthermore, the results obtained in certain cases by the partition method are at variance with those obtained by spectrophotometric and kinetic studies. For example, spectrophotometric study indicates a lack of association between picric acid and s-trinitrobenzene,[97,101] while partition studies point to strong interaction between these compounds. It is probable that the absence of a discrete visible spectrum in this case is due to non-colour-producing London interactions or dipole–dipole interactions.

## 5. Kinetic methods

It is possible to determine the equilibrium concentrations of the various species present during complex formation, and thus the stability constants of the molecular adducts by kinetic methods. The procedures fall broadly into two classes:

(i) The effect of complex formation on reaction rates (direct method).

(ii) The determination of equilibrium concentration of substances which act as *catalysts* in appropriate reactions, the latter being known as "indicator reactions".

There are but few examples in the literature concerning the direct method. For example,[102] aniline and 2,4-dinitrochlorobenzene interact in alcoholic solution to yield aniline hydrochloride and the adduct $2,4\text{-}(O_2N)_2 \cdot C_6H_3 \cdot NH \cdot C_6H_5$. The rate of the reaction is markedly affected by changing the concentrations of the reactants as shown in Table 3.1 ($k_r$ is the velocity constant).

TABLE 3.1. *Kinetics of complex formation in absolute alcohol*

| Concentration (moles/litre) | | $k_r$ |
|---|---|---|
| $C_6H_5 \cdot NH_2$ | $2,4\text{-}(O_2N)_2 - C_6H_3Cl$ | |
| 0·2004 | 0·04993 | 0·262 |
| 1·0106 | 0·04980 | 0·192 |

If butylamine is used instead of aniline there is only a slight increase in the value of the velocity constant (7% instead of the above 27%). This conclusion is supported by the fact that the solution becomes deep yellow in colour, the second rate-constant is reduced if the concentration of aniline is increased, and the velocity constant is not affected if this experiment is carried out in ethyl acetate solution, where no complex formation occurs. Moreover, the kinetic constant thus derived agrees with that obtained by spectroscopic methods.

The application of the indirect catalytic method, involving indicator reactions, may be considered with reference to the indicator and catalytic reactions as follows:

(A) The indicator reaction:

(3.23) $$A + B = P,$$

where $P$ is the product, can proceed in two stages.

(3.24) $$A + B = AB \text{ (fast)}$$

and

(3.25) $$A + B = P \text{ (slow).}$$

The rate of the whole reaction is given by:

(3.26) $$\frac{dx}{dt} = k[AB]$$

and the concentration of $AB$ is obtained from the relation

$$[AB] = \frac{\kappa[B]}{1 + \kappa[B]} \cdot [A]_T,$$

where kappa ($\kappa$) is the stability constant (equilibrium constant of reaction (3.24)), and $[A]_T$ is the total concentration of the reactant $A$.

Let us now consider reaction (3.23) as a catalytic process, viz.

(3.27) $$A + C = CA \text{ (fast)}$$

and

(3.28) $$CA + B = P + C \text{ (slow),}$$

where $C$ is the catalytic species. The concentration of the complex $CA$ may be expressed by

(3.29) $$[CA] = \frac{\kappa[A]}{1 + \kappa[B]}[C],$$

where $[C]$ is the total concentration of the catalyst, and $\kappa$ is now the formation constant of $CA$, i.e. reaction (3.27). Hence,

(3.30) $$\frac{dx}{dt} = \lambda[CA] \cdot [B].$$

On combining the above with eqn. (3.29) we have

(3.31)
$$\frac{dx}{dt} = \lambda \frac{\kappa[A]}{1 + \kappa[A]} \cdot [B] \cdot [C]_T,$$

Therefore

(3.32)
$$\frac{1}{(dx/dt)} = \frac{1}{\lambda[C]_T[B]} + \frac{1}{\lambda[C]_T[B]} \cdot \frac{1}{\kappa} \cdot \frac{1}{[A]}.$$

It is clear that the reciprocal of the reaction rate $(dx/dt)$ is a linear function of the reciprocal of the concentration of the reactant $A$, so that the slope of the graph of $1/[A]$ versus $1/(dx/dt)$ leads to the value for $\kappa$, the stability constant of the complex $CA$.[103] It is worth noting that the Michaelis equation which is applicable to reactions involving enzymes and substrates, is similar to eqn. (3.31).

In many cases complex formation may be accompanied by either an increase or decrease of catalytic activity. For instance, many catalysts lose their catalytic activity owing to their forming complexes with different ligands; the metal ions, are prevented from combining with the catalyst because of the presence of ligands, so that eqn. (3.27) is impossible. On the other hand, an increase in catalytic activity may be due to a number of reasons, such as the orientation of atomic orbitals or the formation of intermediate complexes. In either case it is sometimes possible to determine the stability constants of the complexes (ref. 103, pp. 120–2). In view of the pronounced catalytic activity of many molecular complexes the prospects for the use of the catalytic method for studying complex formation are bright.

## 6. Dielectric polarization and dipole moments

In solutions, which are not appreciably conducting, the molar polarization $P_s$ is given by the relation (ref. 6, 1949)

$$P_s = \frac{\epsilon - 1}{\epsilon + 2} \cdot \frac{\sum_i N_i M_i}{d} = \sum_i N_i P_i,$$

where $\epsilon$ is the measured dielectric constant, $d$ is the density of the solution, $N_i$ is the mole fraction of component $i$, $M_i$ is its molecular weight and $P_i$ its molar polarization. If the calculated values of the molar polarization of a halogen in donor solvents $(P_X)$ are plotted against its mole fraction $N_N$, then the intercept of the curve at $N_X = 0$ gives the molar polarization of the dissolved halogen. It is then found that, in general, $P_X$ increases with the increased strength of the donor. There is,[104, 106, 118, 119] however, no agreement in the literature about the actual values for complexes containing iodine or iodine monochloride in benzene or dioxane. Thus the value of the molar polarization of iodine in benzene ranges in literature from about 38 to about 60 c.c.; in dioxane the corresponding values range from about 66 to about 82 c.c., while that in carbon tetrachloride is nil. The respective value in ICN solvent is considerably higher, while in cyclohexane and di-isobutylene donor solvents the values are reported to be 31 and 75 c.c., respectively. In general, complex formation is indicated by the observed fact that the product of interaction is more polar than either reactant.

Dielectric polarization has been applied to the study of weak 1:1 molecular complexes in concentrated solutions of non-electrolytes, e.g. the aniline–dioxane[105] and iodine–aromatic hydrocarbon systems, the latter in cyclohexane solutions.[106] On the other hand, the interaction between phenol and ether in carbon tetrachloride, benzene or dioxane has been investigated by combining the method of continuous variation with data obtained by dielectric constant measurements.[107] Evidence shows that a complex $2\{C_6H_5OH\}—1\{(C_2H_5)_2O\}$ is formed in carbon tetrachloride or benzene, but none in dioxane; the same conclusions may be reached by infrared spectrophotometry.

Dielectric and optical studies of molecular complexes formed by 1,3,5-trinitrotoluene with hexamethylbenzene[108] show that in carbon tetrachloride solution non-polar mesomery predominates in the ground state, i.e. the resonance energy contribution to the ground state is slight. The ring planes of the reactants are parallel at a distance of $3 \cdot 2$ Å, and the charge-transfer moment is perpendicular to the plane. The polar mesomery part amounts to about 4%, similar to that of the complex formed by hexamethylbenzene with $p$-chloranil.[109] These authors have also investigated the part played by intermolecular resonance in the formation of

$p$-chloranil–$N,N$-dimethylaniline and quinone–$N,N$-dimethylaniline complexes by combining dielectric data with those derived from optical and density studies. Table 3.2 shows the results obtained.

TABLE 3.2. *Intermolecular resonance and complex formation*

| | Compounds | | | |
|---|---|---|---|---|
| | 1,3,5-trinitrobenzene + hexamethylbenzene | Chloranil + hexamethyl- benzene | Chloranil + $N,N$-di- methyl- aniline | Quinone + $N,N$-dimethyl- aniline |
| $k_{eq.}$ (l. mole) | 7·1 | 9·25 | 3·40 | 0·30 |
| $\Delta H_f$ (kcal) | −4·49 | −5·15 | −4·86 | −1·33 |
| $\mu(D)$ | 0·9 | 1·0 | 2·6 | 1·5 |
| $\nu(cm^{-1})$ | 25,400 | 19,350 | 15,400 | 19,800 |

Other complexes investigated by measuring dielectric constants are the (1:1) acetic acid–pyridine and the (2:1) phenol–aniline species[110] and stannic chloride–methanol, stannic chloride-ethanol and stannic chloride–diphenyl ether complexes in benzene solution; alcohol appears to form more than one type (1:2) of molecular complex.[111]

*Dipole moments*

It is found that aluminium bromide or aluminium iodide display large dipole moments in benzene but not in carbon disulphide.[112] Since the interaction products are more polar than the reacting components, it is probable that a molecular complex is formed between the halide and benzene. Similarly, solutions of hydrogen chloride in benzene show a greater dipole moment than does the gaseous chloride.[113] It should be noted, however, that in certain cases the large dipole moment does not arise as a result of interaction between the halide and aromatic nucleus, since the ring substituents may be involved, e.g. stannic chloride or titanic chloride complexes with benzaldehyde or acetophenone.[114] In some cases the dipole moment of the reactant may be reduced, e.g. that of nitrobenzene in the naphthalene–nitrobenzene complex.

The appreciable dipole moments noted during various interactions may sometimes be ascribed to the partial ionic character of the complexes, as in the case of the reaction between benzene and $p$-dinitrobenzene[115] or $s$-trinitrobenzene,[116] where the products are partially ionic in character.[117] This view is supported by the observed lack of additivity of total polarization at radio frequency. Similar considerations apply to the iodine–benzene complexes,[118] the large moment of which is probably due to structures to which polar forms of the type $C_6H_5I^+I^-$ contribute. Hence solutions of iodine in cyclohexane display slight dipole moments, while the moments for benzene, $p$-xylene or dioxane solutions of the halogen are appreciable.

In connection with the behaviour of halogens in various solvents, Fairbrother[118] assumed that the molar polarization of iodine in non-complexing solvents is the sum of the atomic and electronic polarizations of the halogen. He then calculated dipole moments of iodine in complexing solvents (apparent moments) in the usual manner; these were found to be smaller than those (experimental) of the adducts, except for dioxane, because only part of the iodine solute was complexed. The values for iodine and iodine cyanide for various solvents are given in Table 3.3.

TABLE 3.3. *Dipole moments (in debyes) of halogen complexes*

| Solute | Solvents | | | | |
|---|---|---|---|---|---|
| | Carbon tetrachloride | cyclohexane | benzene | dioxane | di-isobutylene |
| Iodine cyanide | 3·64 | 0 | 3·76 | 4·40 | 4·01 |
| Iodine | 0 | 0 | 0·6 | 1·3 | 1·5 |

The value of the dipole moment of the iodine–pyridine complex[106] in cyclo-hexane solution is $4·5D$, while in benzene solution it is $4·17D$;[119] one of the highest values is that given by the triethylamine–iodine complex,[120] which is $11·3D$.

The ionic character of complexes may be calculated by the

application of Mulliken's charge-transfer theory and dipole moments result. Thus the dipole moments of the picrates of aniline, $N,N$-dimethylaniline, ethylamine and $\alpha$- or $\beta$-naphthylamines in dioxane solution, the respective values of which are 6·74, 6·06, 10·37, 5·08 and 6·96$D$, lead on the basis of the Mulliken theory to the conclusion that[121] the direction of charge-transfer is that of the symmetry axis $N^+O^-$; it appears that a "normal" complex $[c = 1, b^2 \approx a^2$ or $b^2 > a^2$ of the wave equation (2.1)] and an "activated" complex $(c = 0·3 \leftrightarrow 0·5)$ are present, but no ion-pairs as postulated previously.[122] Finally, it should be noted that dipole moments (and dielectric constants and densities) are not additive during complex formation, if there is hydrogen bonding between reactants of similar dipole moments.[123]

## 7. Miscellaneous methods

### (i) Viscosity

The occurrence of deviations from ideal behaviour of viscosity isotherms (curves of viscosity versus composition at a constant temperature) indicates complex formation, while the appearance of maxima on these curves points to strong interaction between the moieties. For instance, the viscosity isotherms for solutions of thionyl chloride in mesitylene show a maximum at about 1 : 1 ratio.[124] Similar considerations apply to solutions of arsenious chloride in benzene, nitrobenzene or pyridine,[125] or of antimony trichloride in benzene.[126] In the latter case, a marked maximum occurs at a 1 : 2 donor–acceptor ratio.

A modification of this method consists of plotting the logarithms of viscosity versus percentage composition and observing the slope of the resulting curve.[127] Pospekhov studied the reactions between nicotine and nitrobenzene, o- or p-nitrotoluene, carbon tetrachloride, dichloroethane, bromobenzene and various ketones. Complex formation was indicated by the curve becoming concave towards the $x$-axis or by becoming S-shape. Viscosity measurements have also been used in conjunction with surface tension, parachor and refractive index data to study the 2 : 1 complexes formed by aromatic amines and acetic acid.[128]

An equation derived by Batschinski[129] can also be used for investigating complex formation. The relation may be written in the form

(3.33) $$\eta = B/(v - b),$$

where $v$ is the specific volume and $B$ and $C$ are constants. If it is assumed that $B$ is proportional to the size of the flow units and $b$ is the specific volume of the solid at the melting point, then any deviations from the values for the donor and acceptor moieties may throw some light on structural problems. For instance, the Batschinski constants $B$ for gallium trichloride and pyridine are 0·0575 and 0·0643, respectively, while that for $GaCl_3$-pyridine complex is 0·0763, all values in cp · ml/g mole units. However, these diagnostic deductions are entirely speculative, ·especially as far as the determination of the molecular dimensions is concerned. For example, inorganic bromides have smaller $B$ constants than the corresponding chloride despite the larger size of the bromine atom.

Another viscosity method consists of studying the products of the solvent (donor) and the diffusion coefficient of the acceptor. It is probable that the experimentally determined low values of these products for solutions of iodine in toluene or $m$-xylene, as compared to those of the same halogen in non-aromatic solvents, indicate molecular complex formation.[130]

## (ii) Electrical conductance

An increase of the conductance of a solution of an acceptor in a donor solvent may point to molecular complex formation. For example, solutions of anthracene in hydrogen fluoride,[131] or of bromine in tetraarylethylene[132] conduct electricity. An interesting case is that of the intermediates in the Friedel–Crafts reaction. Thus the solution of aluminium bromide in benzene is non-conducting. However, on adding hydrogen bromide to this solution, a strongly conducting oil is formed.[133] The electrical conductance of this thick oil appears to be due to the complex $C_6H_5H^+AlBr_4^-$ (ref. 85, 1952, **74**, 191).

Among the complexes recently investigated by conductance methods are those of poly-Schiff bases with bromine and iodine. The bases were prepared by polycondensation of glyoxal, dibenzyl or diacetyl with 2,6-diaminopyridine.[172a] The plot of conductance versus composition showed a maximum at the ratio of one donor to two acceptor molecules. These findings were confirmed by ultraviolet electron paramagnetic resonance spectra.

Another example is the interaction between boron trifluoride and number of donors, e.g. ether, alcohols, esters or fatty acids. When gaseous boron trifluoride is bubbled into the liquid acceptor, the conductance of the liquid increases to an enormous extent to a maximum and then drops slightly to a minimum at a composition corresponding to the $1:1$ ratio. The marked increase in conductance implies a high degree of ionization, while the existence of a minimum presupposes complex formation. It must be noted, however, that there is hardly any theoretical justification for the latter statements, though experience indicates that this is true in a number of cases; also, the absence of a minimum does not necessarily imply the absence of complex formation since other factors must also be considered, such as viscosity changes. In general, minima on the conductance–composition isotherms indicate the existence of several complexes. Furthermore, the increase in conductance must be treated with a certain caution, since it may partly or entirely be due to ionized impurities, semi-conductivity or metallic conductivity; the last two types of conductance do not, of course, arise in the case of molten complexes, since they satisfy Faraday's laws of electrolysis and have well-defined decomposition potentials, while the absence of impurities can be established by sample reproducibility studies.[134]

Studies of carefully prepared molten complexes under conditions such that the above-mentioned extraneous conductance effects are absent, revealed that the marked increase in conductance is due to ionic mobility controlled by the size and change of the ions and the viscosity of the medium. The degree of ionic dissociation ($\alpha\%$) is approximately given by the expression[135]

$$(3.34) \qquad \alpha\% \approx \mu\eta,$$

where $\eta$ is the viscosity in centipoises (cp), and $\mu$ is the molar conductance given by the relation

(3.35) $$\mu = \frac{\kappa M}{d},$$

$\kappa$ is the specific conductance, $M$ is the molecular weight and $d$ is the density. The extent of ionic dissociation varies from very low values, e.g. about 0·1% for $BF_3-Et_2O$ via about 30% for $BF_3-2H_2O$ to nearly 100% for gallium dichloride or dibromide. The complete dissociation of the halides is due to the fact that the molten species is in the form $Ga^+[GaBr_4^-]$, i.e. it consists of an equal number of ions in which gallium is univalent and tervalent. This concept of this ionic structure is supported by the fact that the halides are diamagnetic; Raman spectra also lead to the same conclusion.[136]

Another point to be considered is the proton-switch mechanism of conduction.[137] For instance, phosphoric acid conducts by this mechanism, as confirmed by the electrolysis of potassium dihydrogen phosphate in fused phosphoric acid, since the potassium ions do not migrate through the viscous liquid, while the current is carried entirely by a proton-switch involving the phosphoric acid hydrogen-bonded network and the biphosphate ion. However, if this network is broken by introducing the acceptor boron trifluoride, which blocks the lone pair of electrons on the oxygen atoms, then the proton-switch mechanism is replaced by the normal ionic migration process and the molar conductance of the solution will drop from 2·45 to 0·73 mhos cm²/mole; at the same time the viscosity of the solution decreases from 177·4 to 46·2 cp. owing to the virtual destruction of the hydrogen-bonded network. This point of view is reinforced by the fact that the conductances of the hydrogen and deuterium phosphoric acid–boron trifluoride complexes are nearly identical, since the size and mass of the ions which are migrating are only slightly affected; in the case of a proton-switch mechanism the replacement of hydrogen by deuterium would bring about a dramatic drop in conductance, as in the case of pure phosphoric acid. Moreover, the activation energies for conduction and viscous flow for the liquid $H_3PO_4-BF_3$ are very similar, i.e. ionic migration through the medium is the rate-determining process.

An interesting point to be noted in connection with the

application of conductance to the study of complex formation is that concerning the effect of minute concentrations of minor species in equilibrium with the bulk of the liquid. These "impurities" are very difficult to detect by spectroscopic, resonance or diffraction techniques, and their effect on conductance may be considerable. For example, the self-ionization of solvents such as water, sulphur dioxide or ammonia, gives rise to spurious increases in conductance, thus leading to erroneous conclusions regarding the structures of molecular complexes. In certain cases conductivity experiments are combined with electrolysis in order to obtain information about structures. For example, when the molten 1:1 and 1:2 complexes formed by gallium trihalides with pyridine or piperidine are electrolysed, no gaseous products are evolved. Hence the structures cannot be written in the form

$$H^+[C_5H_4N \rightarrow GaCl_3]^-$$

or

$$[C_5H_5NH]^+[C_5H_4N \rightarrow GaCl_3]^-$$

especially since this formulation would imply that the 1:2 adduct could be more stable than the 1:1 complex, contrary to experiment. It is interesting to note that the corresponding 1:2 complexes of boron trifluoride are more stable than those of the 1:1 type; hence gallium complexes seem to be different in structure from the boron ones. Alternative structures are

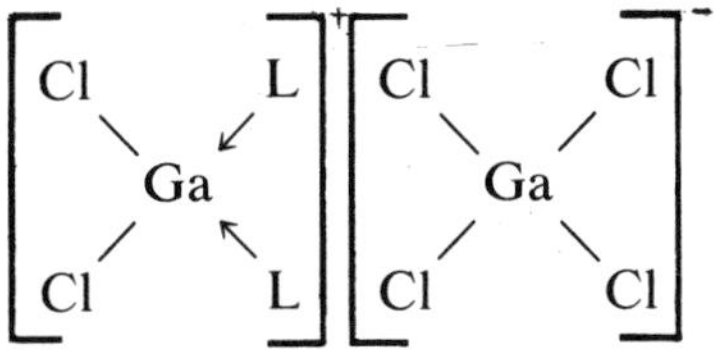

and

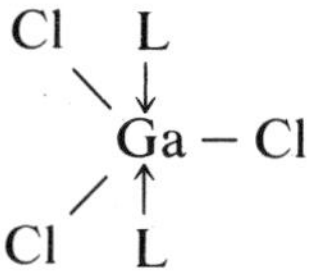

where L is pyridine or piperidine. The latter 1:2 complex can give rise to the 1:1 adduct by the rearrangement of the gallium from trigonal bipyramidal to tetrahedral configuration with the elimination of a chloride ion, viz.

The tetrahedral complex can then combine with a further molecule of gallium trichloride to yield the 1:1 complex, viz.

This formulation is in accord with conductance, electrolytic and stability data of the 1:1 and 1:2 adducts, and points to the following ionization equilibrium of the 1:2 adduct

The case of halogen complexes is of some interest in connection with conductance studies.[132] If the molecular complex is ionic, then the measured conductance of the species in polar solvents is appreciable. For example, the pyridine–halogen complexes show considerable conductance in polar solvents, due to the probable presence of ions, such as $X^-$, $XPy^+$ or $X_3^-$, where X is the halogen and Py is pyridine; the trihalide ion imparts colour to the solution. This interpretation is, however, open to serious objections, since the conductance of the complex increases with time. Similar studies on solutions of bromine in methylene chloride show that the appreciable conductance is probably due to the presence of ions, viz. $Br^-$, $Br_3^-$ and solvent-$Br^+$.

Finally, it is interesting to note that the conductance method can be used for calculating equilibrium constants of molecular complex formation by assuming that the extent of this interaction $\alpha$ is given by the ratio of the equivalent conductance of the solution to that at infinite dilution of the donor moiety.[138]

### (iii) Heats of solution

The study of heats of mixing donor and acceptor compounds can also be used for studying complex formation.[22, 124, 139] Large positive heat effects seem to accompany molecular complex formation, e.g. chloroform with benzene, toluene or mesitylene; 1,3,5-trinitrobenzene with naphthalene in acetone; thionyl chloride with aromatic hydrocarbons.[124] The plots of molal heats of mixing versus composition (mole %) for the various chloroform interaction products are symmetrical, indicating the existence of 1:1 complexes. It is also found that on increasing the methylation of the benzene nucleus, i.e. on passing to toluene and m-xylene, the rate of increase of the magnitudes of the heats of mixing chloroform with the aromatic hydrocarbons diminishes, though the absolute values show an increase. This phenomenon is due to the opposing tendencies of steric hindrance of the methyl groups and inductive effects of the methyl substituents, which enhance the donor capacity of the aromatic hydrocarbons.

The heat of formation $(\Delta H_g)_f$ of a gaseous donor and acceptor can be determined by finding first the heat of formation of the crystalline complex in an excess of the donor and combining the result with the heat of sublimation of the adduct measured by means of a manometer;[140] the heat of formation of the crystalline complex is, of course, obtained by subtracting the heat of solution of the complex in an excess of the donor from that of the acceptor in a similar excess of the donor. For example, the relevant values of $(\Delta H_g)_f$ for the boron trichloride–pyridine and boron trichloride–piperidine complexes are 37·9 and 80·6 kcal/ mole; this indicates greater electron availability on the donor atom in piperidine and thus stronger ligand properties. On the other hand, the heats of formation $(\Delta H_g)_f$ of the pyridine–boron trichloride and pyridine–boron tribromide complexes are 37·9 and 43·5 kcal/mole, so that there is a greater reorganization energy in the trichloride on passing from the planar to the tetrahedral structure.

Other points of interest in connection with the above thermal procedure are as follows:

($\alpha$) It appears that a second mole of a donor is attached less strongly to the acceptor than the first. This is shown, for instance, by the gallium complexes, when the heats of formation (in kcal/mole) for $GaCl_3$–Py and $GaCl_3$–2 Py are 29·8 and 41·5, respectively (the corresponding values for the 1:1 and 1:2 gallium trichloride–piperidine complexes are 33·7 and 52·1).

($\beta$) Nitrogen donors are more exothermic than oxygen donors, e.g. the heats of formation (in kcal/mole) of $GaCl_3$–$Et_2O$ and $GaCl_3$–$C_5H_5N$ are 9·3 and 29·8 respectively.

($\gamma$) The heats of formation of $GaCl_3$–MeCOCl and $GaCl_3$–$Me_2CO$ are 4·1 and 15·3 kcal/mole, respectively. Hence the negative inductive effect of chloride reduces the electron availability at the oxygen atom of the donor moiety to such an extent that the chlorine atom replaces the oxygen atom as the donor atom, so that the acetyl complex is formulated as $MeCO^+GaCl_4^-$, i.e. acetyl tetrachlorogallate.

($\delta$) In certain cases it is also possible to obtain from thermal data the bond dissociation energies of the complexes.[141]

## (iv) Refractive index

The continuous variation method has been applied in conjunction with refractive index measurements to the study of molecular complexes derived from organic and inorganic compounds. For instance, aniline interacts with acetic acid to give a 2:1 and 1:2 complex; toluene seems to interact with benzene to give 1:3 and 3:1 complexes while dioxane ($D$) and water ($W$) give rise to $D:4W$, $D:2W$ and $D:W$ species[142] (Frontas'ev). The refractometric method has been used by Yoshida and Osawa[142] to study complex formation and determine stability constants of the 1:1 adducts formed by phenol with methyl acetate or naphthalene, and alcohol with naphthalene. The aromatic amines–acetic acid interaction has also been studied by Angelescu and Hölszky.[128] Another example concerns aqueous solutions of potassium and strontium or magnesium chloride,[143] when 1 : 1 complexes are formed. This, however, is not found in the case of aqueous solutions of potassium and lithium chlorides, or in methanolic solutions of cerous and ammonium chlorides.

Refractometric measurements of the products of interaction between many organic solutes in carbon tetrachloride solution[144] point to intermolecular hydrogen bonding of the OH ... O, CH ... Cl, CH ... N, OH ...... Cl and ArOH ... ArH types.

### (v) Surface tension

This property of solutions has been used to elucidate the composition of dissolved molecular complexes. For instance, Cagnoli[145] studied the products of interaction between pyrrole (I) and carbon tetrachloride, pyridine (II) and carbon tetrachloride, and mixtures of pyrrole and pyridine (III). He found that in approximately 0·1 M solutions the surface tension varies linearly with concentration in cases I and II where no association occurs, but a distinct minimum occurs in case III, indicating complex formation between pyrrole and pyridine. He extended his investigations to the interaction between cresols and acetophenone,[146] and found that while o-cresol forms a 1 : 1 complex with the ketone, the meta isomer forms 2 : 1, 1 : 1, and 1 : 2 complexes, while the p-cresol forms 2 : 1 and 1 : 1 complexes with the ketone.

Further studies by the same worker[147] include the systems aminopyrine–barbital, antipyrine–diphenols and aminopyrine–diphenols. The first gave a 1 : 1 complex in aqueous solution, while aminopyrine–resorcinol or aminopyrine–pyrocatechol in benzene solution gave 2 : 1, 1 : 1 and 1 : 2 molecular complexes; antipyrine also reacted with hydroquinone in benzene solution to yield 3 : 2 and 2 : 3 complexes. In each case there was a corresponding distinct minimum on the surface tension–composition curve, the surface tension being measured by the ring method.

Another example of the application of this method is that concerning the system acetic acid–aromatic amines.[128]

### (vi) X-ray analysis

The structures of some molecular complexes derived from inorganic and organic moieties have been elucidated by X-ray analysis. For instance, sulphur and stannic iodide combine readily in benzene or carbon disulphide[148] and form Sn $I_4 \cdot 2S_8$ crystals, which are quite stable if kept in sealed glass tubes. X-ray analysis shows that the structure consists of infinite chains of Sn $I_4$ tetrahedra parallel to the $c$-axis of the crystal and bonded together through double $S_8$ rings, each iodine atom being in close proximity to a sulphur atom. The length of the $c$-axis (11·41 Å) shows that charge-transfer interaction is the principal source of stability of the complex, a case similar to that of the tri-iodomethane–sulphur and dithiane–sulphur complexes.[149] The charge-transfer interaction is more intense at higher temperatures hence these complexes become more stable on heating.

X-ray analysis has also been used to study other inorganic complexes, e.g. products of interaction between alkali fluorides and zinc fluoride.[150] While no molecular complex formation appears to take place between lithium fluoride and zinc fluoride, the latter interacts with the fluoride of sodium, potassium, rubidium and caesium to form $M[ZnF_3]$, where $M$ is the alkali metal; in addition, caesium fluoride yields $Cs[Zn_2F_5]$. The X-ray method combined with Phase rule led to the evaluation of their energies and entropies of formation. Complete structure determinations on the complexes of boron trifluoride with amines have been achieved by means of X-ray diffraction analysis,[151] while a number of papers describe the application of this method and study of complexes formed by boron trifluoride with alkali metal compounds.[152] The crystal structure of the complexes $SbCl_5$–$POCl_3$, $SbCl_5$–$(C_6H_5)_2SO$ and $SnCl_4$–$2SeOCl_2$ have been studied in detail,[153] and it has been found that they deviate from ideal octahedral configurations owing to steric effects.

A large number of molecular complexes derived from organic moieties have been examined by X-ray procedures. For example, the 1:1 bromine–acetone solid[154] the quinol–methyl cyanide species similar to quinol clathrates,[155] etc., have been investigated by X-ray analysis. In the case of the trimeric dimethylamino-borine complex it is found that the structure is that of a chair-shaped six-membered ring of alternating $BH_2$ and $NMe_2$ groups with a B–N distance of 1·59 ± 0·02 Å. There are four molecules per unit cell in the orthorhombic crystal, and structural studies lead to the chemical formula $(BH_2)_3(NMe_2)_3$ and not $B_3H_4(NMe_2)_3$ as thought previously.

Crystals of the 1 : 1 molecular complex formed from tricarbonyl-chromiumanisole and 1,3,5-trinitrobenzene were examined by three-dimensional single-crystal X-ray analysis.[192] The benzene rings of the two components were found to be nearly parallel, with perpendicular distances from the aromatic carbon atoms of the anisole molecule to the plane of the trinitrobenzene molecule ranging from 3·34 to 3·50 Å; the rings were shown to be tilted by 25·5° out of the orientation perpendicular to the line joining their centres. In the trinitrobenzene component the ring valency angles at the carbon atoms carrying nitro-groups (123°) were significantly greater than those at the other carbon atoms (117°). The structure of this complex is related to that of other charge-transfer adducts containing aromatic molecules, e.g. 1,3,5-trinitrobenzene with anthracene[193] or azulene,[194] where the donor–acceptor interaction involves $\pi$-electrons of the aromatic rings. However, the greater separation between the moieties in the anisole complex suggests that the aromatic ring charge-transfer interaction is weaker than in the anthracene or indole complexes with trinitrobenzene. This may be attributed to the strong electron-withdrawing capacity of the tricarbonylchromium group leading to a decrease in the donor capacity of the $\pi$-electrons of the anisole molecule. The participation of the latter as electron donor in the solid state complex is thus a function both of the aromatic ring and of the tricarbonylchromium fragment. The assumption of $\sigma$-bond hybridization appears to explain the observed features of the anisole complex.

The halogen molecular complexes have received a great deal of attention in the context of X-ray diffraction studies.[146, 151] Investigations of the benzene-bromine complex[149] Hassel and Strømme) in the range −40° to −50°C showed that the component molecules are alternately arranged in a structure in which the axes of the bromine molecules are nearly perpendicular to the planes of the benzene rings and pass through the symmetry centres of those rings. The bromine–bromine distance in the complex is about the same as in the free halogen molecule, as expected from the weakness of the bond in the complex. The structure is that proposed by Mulliken for an axial model; in solution, however, other structures may be possible.

A number of other complexes involving halogens have also

been investigated by X-ray methods. In the case of the halogen complexes of 1,4-dioxane, 1,4-dithiane, 1,4-diselenane, pyridine, trimethylamine, acetone and dibenzyl sulphide, the $D-X-X$ linkage, where $X$ is the halogen acceptor, is essentially linear; if an interhalogen compound is used, then the donor $D$ is linked to the heavier halogen atom. For example, in the 1,4-dioxane-bromine complex both bromine atoms of the bromine molecule are simultaneously linked to the ether oxygen atoms of different dioxane molecules. On the other hand, both electron pairs of the carbonyl oxygen of acetone can participate in complexing bromine, giving the linear structure $O-Br-Br-O$; the carbons of the methyl group of the ketone do not, however, lie exactly in the plane containing the other atoms of the chain, as shown in Fig. 3.1.

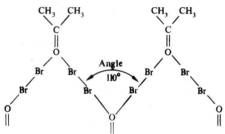

FIG. 3.1 The acetone–bromine complex.

However, the pyridine–ICl is planar, the $Cl-I-N$ linkage being linear and its extension passing through the carbon atom at the opposite side of the ring.

As regards other halogen complexes, the O—$X$ and S—$X$ bonds in the dioxane and dithiane complexes are nearly equatorial, but the $Se-I$ bond in the diselenane complex is in the axial plane. A study of bond distances in various halogen complexes shows that the halogen–donor bond strengths increase in the donor order

$$O < S < Se < N.$$

Another conclusion is that the $N-I$ bonds in pyridine–iodine monochloride, trimethylamine–iodine monochloride and trimethylamine–iodine are nearly as strong as covalent double bonds.

The problem of polymorphism of certain molecular complexes has also received some attention. Thus Matsunaga studied the complexes formed by $p$-chloranil and $p$-bromanil with 1,6-diaminopyrene.[190] These seem to exist in polymorphic forms depending on the method of preparation. His conclusion is supported by evidence obtained by means of X-ray diffraction, diffuse reflectance and absorption spectra, and conductance measurements. Similar considerations apply to the complexes of trichloromonobromo-$p$-benzoquinone and dichlorodibromo-$p$-benzoquinone.

In general, there is an increasing awareness of the potential of X-ray diffraction methods, though the difficulty of isolating many solid molecular complexes is a serious limitation in this field.

### (vii) Ultracentrifuge

In biochemical systems the ultracentrifuge method has been found to be useful in the study of complex formation. For instance, the study of the velocity of sedimentation enabled Singer and others[156] to investigate soluble antigen–antibody complexes by determining the concentrations of *free* antigen in solution. This method is, however, not accurate, since a partial re-equilibration may occur during sedimentation, resulting in a broadening of the boundaries. Furthermore, no attempt has so far been made to determine the relevant stability constants of these biochemical complexes.

### (viii) Parachor

The concept of the parachor has been applied to the study of complex formation.[157] It was found, for instance, that in the case of chloroform–methanol or chloroform–acetone mixtures complex formation is indicated by a negative difference between the experimental and theoretical values of the parachor. Another example is that involving aromatic amines–acetic acid interactions.[128] It must be stressed, however, that the use of this method is open to serious objections. Indeed, the parachor is rather a lame criterion for the existence of complexes in solution. On the other hand, measurements of the apparent molar volumes[89] have been used by Jepson and Rowlinson to study complexes formed by iodine with organic solvents. The apparent molar volume of dissolved iodine appears to be smaller in complexing than in non-complexing solvents. The solvents used may be arranged in the following order, corresponding to decreasing molar volume of the dissolved halogen:

$c$-hexane > benzene > mesitylene > pyridine > diethyl ether.

### (ix) Electrophoresis

Electrophoresis (moving-boundary) method has mainly been used[156,158] in the biochemical field, e.g. antigen–antibody complex or ovalbumin–nucleic acid system. A modified technique, known as crossing paper electrophoresis[159] has been applied to the study of dye systems, e.g. methylene blue–bromocresol green, fuchsin–bromophenol blue, fuchsin–orange GG, etc. This procedure consists of applying drops of solutions of the compounds to a filter paper in a Grassmann type apparatus; a deformation at the crossing point indicates interaction. A related technique is that of two-dimension chromatography[160] using the same solvent; any substance that changes deviates from the diagonal path.

### (x) Other procedures

Other procedures used for studying molecular complexes are electrolysis[161] and ultrasonics;[162] the latter has mainly been used for investigating carbon dioxide–air or carbon dioxide–oxygen gaseous systems. It is worth noting that anomalous changes in ultrasonic vibrations with composition are not always related to complex formation.[163] Another important procedure is that involving light scattering, as in the case of antigen–antibody[164] and antigen–hapten[165] systems. A similar technique is the application of combination scattering of light for solutions of aniline in mineral and organic acids,[166] and of complexes of the acceptor 2,3-dichloro-5,6-dicyanobenzoquinone.[167] The latter acceptor has a high electrode potential ($E_0 \approx 1$ volt) and, therefore, gives rise to strong molecular complexes;[168] thus $p$-phenylenediamine yields a $1:1$ complex with the quinone acceptor, which gives in methylene chloride solution strong optical absorption. The complex resembles that of $p$-chloranil by giving a strong e.s.r. signal and a positive Seebeck coefficient, thus indicating that holes are the majority carriers.

It is interesting to note that the carbonyl frequency of this acceptor at 1700 cm$^{-1}$ disappears on complex formation and a characteristic infrared spectrum appears which is different from that of the components. The increase in absorption in the region below $2\,\mu$ is due to electronic transitions, and this points to the existence of an ionic complex.[169] It is worth noting that the above considerations do not apply to the complexes formed by perylene or pyrene with the above acceptor for the Seebeck coefficient is negative; the carriers being electrons and not holes, and there is no e.s.r. signal. This behaviour of the diamine complex is probably due to the fact that about 10% of the molecules exist as ion-radicals. Another example of such a complex is $N,N,N',N'$-tetramethyl-$p$-phenylenediamine.[170]

Nuclear magnetic resonance of polar molecules in aromatic solvents[171] and electron-spin resonance of solid paramagnetic molecular complexes such as biradicals and ion-radicals,[172] are being increasingly used for the study of molecular complexes. The relation between charge-transfer and paramagnetism of the complexes[173] formed by chloranil with $p$-xylene or $N,N$-dimethylaniline in $n$-heptane solution has also been investigated by electron-spin resonance and optical spectra, while magneto-chemical studies of the paramagnetism of triphenylmethane dyes[174] point to complex formation between the flat-packed dye cations. Another method used is based on measurements of the static polarization of ternary systems, e.g. acetone–chloroform–carbon tetrachloride, or acetic acid–dioxane–carbon tetrachloride;[175] in this case, the experimental results obtained agree with those derived theoretically.

Paramagnetic and magnetic susceptibility properties of substances formed in interactions between donors and acceptors have been studied in the context of complex formation. The complex $p$-bromanil-$p$-phenylenediamine[176] was investigated by various methods, including paramagnetism and was found to be a 1:1 complex in benzene solution; this simple molecular ratio does not, however, obtain in a methylene chloride solution. Another example[170,172] concerns aromatic diamines and substituted $p$- and $o$-benzoquinones, viz. the complex TMPD–

TCNQ, where TMPD is $N,N,N',N'$-tetramethyl-$p$-phenyl-enediamine and TCNQ is 7,7,8,8-tetracyano-$p$-quinodimethane (ref. 172). This complex can be prepared by reacting TMPD$^+$-$ClO_4^-$ with $Li^+TCNQ^-$; the constituent ions of the substance are positive and negative paramagnetic ions in contrast to the well-known anion radical salts,[177] TCNQ, in which the positive ion is diamagnetic. Confirmatory evidence has been obtained by electron-spin resonance procedures.

Magnetic susceptibility procedures have been adapted for studying molecular complex formation involving halogens. For instance, the susceptibility of the iodine–benzene complex is greater than that of the sum of the constituents[178] while the formation of polycyclic aromatic hydrocarbons–halogen complexes in solution or in the solid state is accompanied by marked changes in magnetic susceptibility.[46] However, these exhibit high electrical conductance and are probably paramagnetic.

The complexes formed by poly-Schiff bases with halogens were investigated by means of electron paramagnetic resonance spectra.[172a] In all these complexes a single line ($g \sim 2\cdot001$–$2\cdot002$) was found that obeyed Curie's law at temperatures between 77°K and 298°K. The estimated number of paramagnetic centres was in the range $10^{-5}$–$10^{-2}$ of the number of molecules, these centres being local in character. This method was also used for the study of $p$-chloranil-$p$-phenylenediamine complexes[191] and those formed when polycyclic hydrocarbons or alkyl benzenes are adsorbed on platinum dioxide or palladium monoxide surfaces. The electron paramagnetic spectra can be correlated with the ability of these oxides to catalyse exchange reactions.[172b]

The kinetics of complex formation in the case of tetracyano-ethylene and dimethylsulphoxide were investigated by electron paramagnetic resonance.[186] This strong complex, which absorbs at 372 m$\mu$ and has a stability constant of 95·4 at room temperature, gives a signal that increases to a maximum and then decays in accordance with second order kinetics. The initial intensity of this signal is proportional to the concentration of tetracyano-ethylene in dimethyl sulphoxide.

In general, not all of the above described methods can be applied to a particular problem. Thus, to investigate the structure of a given complex it is essential to use a combination of a few appropriate procedures. For example, the structure of boron trifluoride dihydrate cannot be investigated by diffraction or resonance techniques, except nuclear magnetic resonance, or by magnetochemistry. On the other hand, electrolysis, conductivity and vibrational spectra are useful in this case. In fact a number of special methods have been developed for the molecular complexes of Group III elements, as shown below.

### (8)  Special methods as applied to Group III elements

In view of the importance of molecular complexes containing boron, aluminium and other elements of Group III of the Periodic Table, special procedures, in addition to those described previously, have been applied to determine their stabilities. In this connection the strength of the metal–ligand bond has been defined as the enthalpy change of the gas-phase dissociation of the molecular complex, viz. $\Delta H$ of the reaction.[179]

$$D \cdot MX_3(g) \rightleftharpoons D(g) + MX_3(g)$$

where $D$ is the donor and $M$ is the Group III element acting as an acceptor. Since the equilibrium constant $K_p$ is a measure of the free-energy change $\Delta G°(\Delta G° = -RT \ln K_p)$, it is possible that the dissociation of a complex $(A)$ having a thermodynamic dissociation (equilibrium) constant $(K_p)_A$ at a given temperature may be associated with a greater enthalpy change $(\Delta H)_A$ than $(\Delta H)_B$, corresponding to a complex $(B)$ having a smaller dissociation constant $(K_p)_B$ at the same temperature. On the other hand, $(\Delta H)_A < (\Delta H)_B$ for the two complexes, provided that the entropies of dissociation in both reactions are similar $((\Delta S)_A \approx (\Delta S_B))$, since $\Delta G = \Delta H - T\Delta S$. Care is thus necessary when using $K$p as a measure of stability.

The procedures used are as follows:

(i)  *Thermal dissociation.* Since gas-phase studies can be carried out at different temperatures, it is possible to calculate the thermodynamic function of dissociation,[180] i.e. $\Delta H$, $\Delta S$ and $\Delta G°$. An extensive compilation of such data has been made by Stone (see ref. 179, pp. 106–7); the equilibrium constants can, of course, be calculated from the thermodynamic data. This method is, however, unsuitable for the study of complexes for which the degree of dissociation exceeds 90% or where there is little dissociation at even relatively elevated temperatures (*ca.* 170°C).

(ii) *Calorimetry.* This method has mainly been applied to complexes of boron in solution, the reactant moieties being liquids or gases; the experimental results are usually combined with other data, such as heats of solution, vaporization or sublimation in order to obtain values of enthalpy changes in the gaseous state; these changes are assumed to represent dative-bond strengths. It has been found, in general, that[181] the heat of formation of a molecular complex in solution is similar to the heat of dissociation in the gaseous phase, though some exceptions exist,[182] e.g. for the product of interaction between aliphatic mono-alkyl-amines with boron trimethyl the order of variation of the enthalpy changes is different from that of the equilibrium constant[180, 183] (formation constants). This work has been extensively reviewed by Brown *et al.*[180–184]

(iii) *Displacement reactions.* This procedure gives only a qualitative indication of the stability constants and has been found to be useful in the case of stable complexes. The method consists of displacing a donor or acceptor in a molecular complex by means of another donor or acceptor. This is, however, complicated by a number of factors, such as lattice energies, volatilization and entropy effects, though the effect of lattice energies and entropies is very small.

(iv) *Relative volatility.* This method involves the measurement of saturation pressures, since in the case of molecular complexes of similar type and molecular weight, the stabilities decrease as the saturation pressures increase.[185] As regards complexes of widely different molecular weights, higher pressures indicate greater dissociation, because the "lighter" complexes are expected to be more volatile.

### References

1. L. Michaelis and S. Granick, *J. Amer. Chem. Soc.*, 1944, **66**, 1023.
2. W. Dilthey and P. Wizinger, *J. Pract. Chem.*, 1928, **118**, 346; O. L. Baril and E. S. Hauber, *J. Amer. Chem. Soc.*, 1931, **53**, 1087.

3. W. H. HUNTER and E. H. NORTHEY, *J. Phys. Chem.*, 1933, **37**, 875.
4. D. F. EVANS, *J. Chem. Soc.*, 1953, 345; id. ibid., 1961, 1987, 2566.
5. M. A. SLIFKIN, *Nature (London)*, 1962, **193**, 464.
6. H. BENESI and J. H. HILDEBRAND, *J. Amer. Chem. Soc.*, 1948, **70**, 2832; id. ibid., 1949, **71**, 2703.
7. O. J. WALKER, *Trans. Faraday Soc.*, 1935, **31**, 432.
8. R. F. HUNTER *et al.*, *J. Chem. Soc.*, 1936, 1576.
9. L. DEDE and A. ROSENBERG, *Ber.*, 1934, **67B**, 147.
10. N. S. BAYLISS and C. J. BRACKENRIDGE, *J. Amer. Chem. Soc.*, 1955, **77**, 3959.
11. D. F. EVANS, *J. Chem. Soc.*, 1957, 4229.
12. S. D. ROSS and M. M. LABES, *J. Amer. Chem. Soc.*, 1957, **79**, 76.
13. H. E. UNGNADE *et al.*, *J. Phys. Chem.*, 1960, **64**, 1410.
14. M. CHOWDHURY, *J. Phys. Chem.*, 1962, **66**, 353.
15. G. BRIEGLEB, *Pure Appl. Chem.*, 1962, **4**, 105.
16. W. N. WHITE, *J. Amer. Chem. Soc.*, 1959, **81**, 2912.
17. R. S. MULLIKEN and L. E. ORGEL, *J. Amer. Chem. Soc.*, 1957, **79**, 4839.
18. J. CZEKALLA *et al.*, *Z. Elektrochem.*, 1957, **61**, 537.
19. E. K. PLYLER and D. R. WILLIAMS, *Phys. Rev.*, 1936, **49**, 215; W. GORDY, *J. Chem. Phys.*, 1941, **9**, 215.
20. A. N. TERENIN and N. YAROSLAVSKII, *Acta Physicochim. URSS*, 1942, **17**, 240.
21. W. R. BURTON and R. E. RICHARDS, *J. Chem. Soc.*, 1950, 1316.
22. M. TAMRES, *J. Amer. Chem. Soc.*, 1952, **75**, 3375; L. H. JONES and R. M. BADGER, ibid., 1951, **73**, 3132.
23. R. A. ZINGARO *et al.*, *J. Amer. Chem. Soc.*, 1951, **73**, 88.
24. D. CASSIMATIS and B. P. SUSZ, *Helv. Chim. Acta*, 1961, **44**, 943.
25. W. SCHLENK, jun., *Fortschr. Chem. Forschung*, 1951, **2**, 92.
26. H. A. BENESI, *J. Amer. Chem. Soc.*, 1953, **75**, 2250.
27. D. L. GLUSKER and H. W. THOMPSON, *J. Chem. Soc.*, 1955, 471.
28. E. GRUNWALD and W. C. COBURN, *J. Amer. Chem. Soc.*, 1958, **80**, 1322; I. PRIGOGINE, *J. Chim. Phys.*, 1948, **45**, 17.
29. N. FUSON *et al.*, *J. Chim. Phys.*, 1958, **55**, 454.
30. J. FUSON and M. L. JOSIEN, *J. Phys. Radium*, 1954, **15**, 652; N. FUSON, *J. Chim. Phys.*, 1958, **55**, 458; S. N. VINOGRADOV and R. H. LINNELL, *J. Chem. Phys.*, 1955, **23**, 93.
31. G. M. BARROW and E. A. YERGER, *J. Amer. Chem. Soc.*, 1954, **76**, 5247; M. L. JOSIEN *et al.*, *Bull. Soc. Chim. France*, 1958, 188; R. C. LORD *et al.*, *J. Amer. Chem. Soc.*, 1955, **77**, 1365.
32. P. GAGNAUX *et al.*, *Helv. Chim. Acta*, 1958, **41**, 1322.
33. B. P. SUSZ and P. CHALANDON, *Helv. Chim. Acta*, 1958, **41**, 1322; B. P. SUSZ and H. LACHAVANNE, ibid., 1958, **41**, 634.
34. B. P. SUSZ and P. CHALANDON, *Helv. Chim. Acta*, 1958, **41**, 697.
35. J. GOUBEAU and W. BUES, *Z. anorg. Chem.*, 1952, **268**, 221.
36. H. GERDING *et al.*, *Rec. Trav. Chim.*, 1952, **71**, 501.
37. J. LACOMBE *et al.*, *Bull. Soc. Chim. France*, 1959, **1959**, 1175.
38. H. F. PRIEST and W. C. SCHUMB, *J. Amer. Chem. Soc.*, 1948, **70**, 2291.
39. C. D. SHMULBACH and R. S. DRAGO, *J. Amer. Chem. Soc.*, 1960, **82**, 4484.
40. V. D. GOL'TSEV, *Zh. Fiz. Khim.*, 1962, **36**, 364.
41. P. JOB, *Ann. Chim.*, 1928, **9**, 113.
42. W. C. VOSBURGH and G. R. COOPER, *J. Amer. Chem. Soc.*, 1941, **63**, 437;

J. Rose, *Dynamic Physical Chemistry*, Pitman, London, 1961; id., *Advanced Physico-Chemical Experiments*, Pitman, London, 1964.

43. P. D. Bartlett and K. Nozaki, *J. Amer. Chem. Soc.*, 1946, **68**, 1497; C. Walling *et al.*, ibid., 1948, **70**, 1533; E. R. Garrett and R. L. Guile, ibid., 1953, **75**, 3958.

44. B. R. Hamilton and D. LL. Hammick, *J. Chem. Soc.*, 1938, 1350.

45. T. T. Davies and D. LL. Hammick, *J. Chem. Soc.*, 1938, 763.

46. S. P. McGlynn, *Chem. Revs.*, 1958, **58**, 1131.

47. D. D. Eley and P J. King, *J. Chem. Soc.*, 1952, 4972.

48. L. J. Andrews and R. M. Keefer, *J. Amer. Chem. Soc.*, 1951, **73**, 4169.

49. L. J. Andrews and R. M. Keefer, *J. Amer. Chem. Soc.*, 1951, **73**, 462.

50. L. J. Andrews and R. M. Keefer, *J. Amer. Chem. Soc.*, 1950, **72**, 5170; id. ibid., 1952, **74**, 4500.

51. B. D. Saksena and R. E. Kagavise, *J. Chem. Phys.*, 1951, **19**, 994.

52. W. G. Barb, *Trans. Faraday Soc.*, 1953, **49**, 143; L. J. Andrews and R. M. Keefer, *J. Amer. Chem. Soc.*, 1953, **75**, 3776.

53. P. R. Hammond, *Nature (London)*, 1964, **201**, 922.

54. J. Landauer and H. McConnell, *J. Amer. Chem. Soc.*, 1952, **74**, 1221; R. Foster *et al.*, *J. Chem. Soc.*, 1953, 3817.

55. T. M. Cromwell and R. L. Scott, *J. Amer. Chem. Soc.*, 1950, **72**, 3825.

56. J. A. A. Ketelaar *et al.*, *Rec. Trav. Chim.*, 1952, **71**, 1104.

57. S. Nagakura, *J. Amer. Chem. Soc.*, 1958, **80**, 520.

58. R. L. Scott, *Rec. Trav. Chim.*, 1956, **75**, 787.

59. L. I. Katzin and R. L. McBeth, *J. Phys. Chem.*, 1958, **62**, 253.

60. H. D. Anderson and D. LL. Hammick, *J. Chem. Soc.*, 1950, 1089; S. D. Ross *et al.*, *J. Amer. Chem. Soc.*, 1956, **78**, 343; R. Foster, *J. Chem. Soc.*, 1957, 5098; J. A. A. Ketelaar and Van de Stolpe, *Rec. Trav. Chim.*, 1952, **71**, 805.

61. S. E. Wood *et al.*, *J. Phys. Chem.*, 1957, **61**, 1605.

62. N. J. Rose and R. S. Drago, *J. Amer. Chem. Soc.*, 1959, **81**, 6138, 6141; J. Rose, *Advanced Physico-Chemical Experiments*, Pitman, London, 1964, pp. 267–9.

63. S. Nagakura, *J. Amer. Chem. Soc.*, 1954, **76**, 3070.

64. A. I. Popov *et al.*, *J. Amer. Chem. Soc.*, 1960, **82**, 1850.

65. L. J. Andrews and R. M. Keefer, *J. Amer. Chem. Soc.*, 1952, **74**, 640; id. ibid., 1953, **75**, 3561.

66. H. Gerding *et al.*, *Spectrochim. Acta*, 1960, **16**, 881.

67. P. Pineau *et al.*, *J. Chim. Phys.*, 1958, **55**, 464.

68. G. Dallinga, *Acta Cryst.*, 1954, **7**, 665; H. Akamatsu *et al.*, *Bull. Chem. Soc. Japan*, 1957, **30**, 618.

69. R. E. Merriefield and W. D. Phillips, *J. Amer. Chem. Soc.*, 1958, **80**, 2778.

70. S. Yamashita, *Bull. Chem. Soc. Japan*, 1959, **32**, 1212.

71. D. A. Wenz, *Ann Arbor, Mich., Diss. Abstr.*, 1961, **22**, 1402.

72. Y. Amako, *Sci. Repts.*, Tohoku Univ., 1st. series, 1956, **40**, 147; H. Yada *et al.*, *Bull. Chem. Soc. Japan*, 1960, **33**, 1660.

73. W. R. Burnham and W. M. Madgin, *J. Chem. Soc.*, 1936, 1303; id. ibid., 1937, 606; P. Chiorboli and G. Morisi, *Gazz. Chim. Ital.*, 1954, **84**, 1066; H. M. Glass and W. M. Madgin, *J. Chem. Soc.*, 1933, 143, 193; id. ibid., 1934, 260, 1292.

74. D. D. Eley and P. J. King, *Trans. Faraday Soc.*, 1951, **47**, 1287.

75. N. N. GREENWOOD and R. L. MARTIN, *Quart Revs. (London)*, 1954, **8**, 11.
76. D. COOK *et al.*, *Can. J. Research*, 1956, 957.
77. N. A. PUSHKIN *et al.*, *Bull. Chem. Soc., Roy. Yougoslav*, 1936, **7**, 73; E. G. SHRIRO, *Khim. Referat. Zh.*, 1938, **1**, 15; V. A. PLOTNIKOV and N. N. GRATSIANSKI, *J. Gen. Chem. USSR*, 1939, **9**, 1057; id. ibid., 1945, **15**, 596; T. SINOMIYA, *Bull. Chem. Soc. Japan*, 1940, **15**, 92, 137, 259, 281, 309; C. C. ADDISON and J. C. SHELDON, *J. Chem. Soc.*, 1956, 2709; R. P. RASTOGI and R. K. NIGAM, *J. Sci. Ind. Res. (Indian)*, 1959, **18B**, 305; R. R. HOLMES, *J. Phys. Chem.*, 1960, **64**, 1295.
78. T. N. SUMAROKOVA, *Zh. Neorg. Khim.*, 1960, **5**, 1572.
79. C. MAZZETTI and F. DE CARLI, *Gazz. Chim. Ital.*, 1926, **56**, 34; F. DE CARLI, *Atti Acad. Lincei*, 1926, **4**, 460, 523; W. F. SEYER and W. S. PECK, *J. Amer. Chem. Soc.*, 1930, **52**, 14.
80. A. F. KAPUSTINSKIĬ and S. I. DRAKIN, *Bull. Acad. Sci. URSS, Classe Sci. Chim.*, 1947, 435.
81. A. KOFLER, *Z. phys. Chem.*, 1940, **A187**, 201.
82. A. KOFLER, *Z. phys. Chem.*, 1940, **A187**, 363; id. ibid., 1942, **A190**, 287; id., *Z. Elektrochem.*, 1944, **50**, 200.
83. A. F. KAPUSTINSKIĬ and V. A. MALTSEV, *J. Phys. Chem. USSR*, 1940, **14**, 105; S. J. O'BRIEN *et al.*, *J. Amer. Chem. Soc.*, 1939, **61**, 2504; S. J. O'BRIEN and E. G. BOBALEK, ibid., 1940, **62**, 3227; S. J. O'BRIEN and J. B. BYRNE, ibid., 1940, **62**, 2063; S. J. O'BRIEN and C. L. KENNY, ibid., 1940, **62**, 1189; S. J. O'BRIEN, ibid., 1941, **63**, 2709; R. F. WEIMER and J. M. PRAUSNITZ, *J. Chem. Phys.*, 1965, **42**, 3643.
84. G. WEISSENBERGER and F. SCHUSTER, *Monatschr. Chem.*, 1924, **45**, 413; G. WEISSENBERGER *et al.*, ibid., 1924, **45**, 425; id. ibid., 1925, **46**, 295, 306, 482; G. WEISSENBERGER and L. PIATTI, ibid., 1924, **45**, 281.
85. H. C. BROWN *et al.*, *J. Amer. Chem. Soc.*, 1950, **72**, 5347; H. C. BROWN and H W. PEARSALL, ibid., 1952, **74**, 191.
86. M. L. MCGLASHAN and R. P. RASTOGI, *Trans. Faraday Soc.*, 1958, **54**, 496.
87. H. ULICH, *Z. phys. Chem.*, Bodenstein Festband, 1931, 423; R. E VAN DYKE, *J. Amer. Chem. Soc.*, 1950, **72**, 3169; H. C. BROWN and W. J. WALLACE, ibid., 1953, **75**, 6265, 6268.
88. L. J. ANDREWS, *Chem. Revs.*, 1954, **54**, 722.
89. H. C. BROWN and J. D. BRADY, *J. Amer. Chem. Soc.*, 1949, **71**, 3573; id. ibid., 1952, **74**, 3520; J. H. HILDEBRAND and R. L. SCOTT, *Solubility of Non-Electrolytes*, 3rd ed., Reinhold, New York, 1950, p. 272; W. P. JEPSON and J. S. ROWLINSON, *J. Chem. Soc.*, 1956, 1278; J. H. HILDEBRAND and D. N. GLEW, *J. Phys. Chem.*, 1956, **60**, 618; G. KORTÜM and W. M. VOGEL, *Z. Elektrochem.*, 1955, **59**, 16.
90. D. A. MCCAULAY *et al.*, *Ind. Eng. Chem.*, 1950, **42**, 2103; D. A. MCCAULAY and A. P. LIEN, *J. Amer. Chem. Soc.*, 1951, **73**, 2013.
91. R. BEHREND, *Z. phys. Chem.*, 1892, **9**, 405; id. ibid., 1892, **10**, 265; id. ibid., 1894, **15**, 183; B. KURILOFF, ibid., 1895, **23**, 419; id. ibid. 1897, **25**, 90.
92. J. H. SIMONS, *J. Amer. Chem. Soc.*, 1931, **53**, 831; W. KLATT, *Z. anorg. u. allgem. Chem.*, 1937, **234**, 189; L. C. HAMMETT, *Physical Organic Chemistry*, McGraw-Hill, New York, 1940.
93. J. H. HILDEBRAND, *J. Phys. and Colloid. Chem.*, 1949, **53**, 973; R. L. BOHON and W. F. CLASSEN, *J. Amer. Chem. Soc.*, 1951, **73**, 1571.
94. B. ARENDS, *Ber. deut. Chem. Ges.*, 1931, **64B**, 1936.
95. H. LEY and R. GRAU, *Ber. deut. Chem. Ges.*, 1928, **58B**, 1765.

96. L. J. ANDREWS and R. M. KEEFER, *J. Amer. Chem. Soc.*, 1949, **71**, 3644; id. ibid., 1950, **72**, 3113, 5034.
97. T. S. MOORE *et al.*, *J. Chem. Soc.*, 1931. 1447.
98. C. GOLUMBIC, *J. Amer. Chem. Soc* , 1952, **74**, 5777.
99. S. WINSTEIN and H. J. LUCAS, *J. Amer. Chem. Soc.*, 1938, **60**, 836; F. R. HEPNER *et al.*, ibid., 1952, **74**, 1333.
100. C. GOLUMBIO and S. WELLER, *J. Amer. Chem. Soc.*, 1952, **74**, 3739.
101. S. D. Ross and I. KUNTZ, *J. Amer. Chem. Soc.*, 1954, **76**, 74.
102. S. D. Ross and I. KUNTZ, *J. Amer. Chem. Soc.*, 1954, **76**, 3000.
103. K. B. YATSIMIRSKII, *Co-ordination Chemistry, 7th Intern. Conf. on Co-ordination Chemistry (1962)*, Butterworth, London, 1963, p. 118.
104. J. R. WILLIAMS and R. J. ALLGEIER, *J. Amer. Chem. Soc.*, 1927, **49**, 2416; K. MÜLLER, *Z. Physik*, 1933, **34**, 689; S. KAFTANOW *et al.*, *Acta Physicochem. URSS*, 1937, **7**, 75.
105. A. V. FEW and J. W. SMITH, *J. Chem. Soc.*, 1949, 753, 2781.
106. G. KORTÜM and H. WALZ, *Z. Elektrochem.*, 1953, **57**, 73.
107. F. OEHME, *Chem. Tech. Berlin*, 1955, **7**, 525.
108. G BRIEGLEB and J. CZEKALLA, *Naturw.*, 1954, **41**, 448.
109. G. BRIEGLEB and J. CZEKALLA, *Z. Elektrochem.*, 1954, **58**, 249.
110. C. ABGRALL and R. BARRÉ, *Compt. Rend.*, 1961, **253**, 439.
111. E. N. GUR'YANOVA and I. P. GOLDSHTEIN, *Zh. Obshch. Khim.*, 1962, **32**, 12.
112. H. ULICH and W. NESPITAL, *Z. Elektrochem.*, 1931, **37**, 559; id., *Angew. Chem.*, 1931, **44**, 750; W. NESPITAL, *Z. phys. Chem.*, 1932, **B16**, 153.
113. F. FAIRBROTHER, *J. Chem. Soc.*, 1932, 43; id. ibid., 1933, 1541.
114. H. ULICH *et al.*, *Z. phys. Chem.*, 1932, **B17**, 21.
115. G. BRIEGLEB and J. KAMBEITZ, *Z. phys. Chem.*, 1934, **B25**, 253; id., *Naturw.*, 1934, **22**, 105.
116. C. J. LEFÈVRE and R. J. W. LEFÈVRE, *J. Chem. Soc.*, 1935, 957.
117. J. WEISS, *J. Chem. Soc.*, 1942, 245; H. KRONBERGER and J. WEISS, ibid., 1944, 464; R. C. SAHNEY *et al.*, *J. Indian Chem. Soc.*, 1949, **26**, 329.
118. F. FAIRBROTHER, *Nature*, 1947, **160**, 87; id., *J. Chem. Soc.*, 1948, 1051.
119. Y. K. SYRKIN and K. M. ANISIMOVA, *Dokl. Akad. Nauk SSSR*, 1948, **59**, 1457.
120. H. TSUBOMURA and S. NAGAKURA, *J. Chem. Phys.*, 1957, **27**, 819.
121. R. RAMAN and S. SOUNDARARAJAN, *Can. J. Chem.*, 1961, **39**, 1247.
122. H. TSUBOMURA, *Bull. Chem. Soc. Japan*, 1958, **31**, 435.
123. A. E. LUTSKII and E. M. OBUKHOVA, *Zh. Obshch. Khim.*, 1961, **31**, 2692, 2709.
124. G. H. LOCKET, *J. Chem. Soc.*, 1932, 1501.
125. M. P. SHUL'GINA, *J. Gen. Chem. USSR*, 1934, **4**, 225; B. P. KONDRATENKO, ibid., 1934, **4**, 244.
126. N. K. VOSKRESENSKAYA *et al.*, *Chem. Abstr.*, 1946, **40**, 3047.
127. D. A. POSPEKHOV, *Trudy Odessk. Selskhkhoz. Instit.*, 1957, **9**, 59.
128. E. ANGELESCU and C. HÖLSZKY, *Anable Univ. C. I. Parhon Bucuresti, Ser. stiint. nat.*, 1956, 113.
129. H. J. BATSCHINSKI, *Z. phys. Chem.*, 1913, **84**, 643.
130. R. H. STOKES *et al.*, *Trans. Faraday Soc.*, 1953, **49**, 886.
131. W. KLATT, *Z. anorg. allgem. Chem.*, 1935, **222**, 225.
132. R. E. BUCKLES and N. A. MEINHARDT, *J. Amer. Chem. Soc.*, 1952, **74**, 1171, G. KORTÜM and H. WILSKI, *Z. phys. Chem.*, 1953, **202**, 35.
133. E. WERTYPOROCH and B. ADAMUS, *Z. phys. Chem.*, 1933, **A168**, 31.

134. N. N. GREENWOOD, *Co-ordination Chemistry, 7th Intern. Conf. on Co-ordination Chemistry (1962)*, Butterworth, London, 1963.
135. N. N. GREENWOOD and R. L. MARTIN, *J. Chem. Soc.*, 1953, 1427.
136. L. A. WOODWARD *et al.*, *J. Chem. Soc.*, 1956, 3723; L. A. WOODWARD *et al.*, ibid., 1958, 1505.
137. N. N. GREENWOOD and A. THOMPSON, *J. Chem. Soc.*, 1959, 3474, 3485, 3493, 3864.
138. M. KILPATRICK and F. E. LUBORSKI, *J. Amer. Chem. Soc.*, 1953, **75**, 577.
139. V. KIREJEW, *J. Phys. Chem. USSR*, 1937, **10**, 298; K. SUZUKI and S. SEKI, *Bull. Chem. Soc. Japan*, 1955, **28**, 417; K. HARTLEY and H. A. SKINNER, *Trans. Faraday Soc.*, 1950, **46**, 621.
140. N. N. GREENWOOD and P. G. PERKINS, *Pure and Appl. Chem.*, 1961, **2**, 55.
141. F. A. COTTON and J. R. LETO, *J. Chem. Phys.*, 1959, **30**, 993; N. N. GREENWOOD, *Advances in Inorg. Chem. and Radiochem.*, ed. H. J. EMELÉUS and A. G. SHARPE, vol. 5, Acad. Press, New York, 1963.
142. V. P. FRONTAS'EV, *Referat. Zh. Khim.*, 1957, Abstr. No. 358; Z. YOSHIDA and E. OSAWA, *Bull. Chem. Soc. Japan*, 1965, **38**, 140.
143. N. F. ERMOLENKO *et al.*, *Uchenye Zapiski Belorus. Gosudarst. Univ. im. V. I. Lenina, Ser. Khim.*, 1956, No. 29, 251; N. F. ERMOLENKO and KH. YA. LEVITMAN, *Zh. Neorg. Khim.*, 1956, **1**, 1162.
144. C. H. GILES *et al.*, *J. Chem. Soc.*, 1961, 5434.
145. N. CAGNOLI, *Ann. Chim. (Rome)*, 1958, **48**, 839.
146. N. CAGNOLI, *Ann. Chim. (Rome)*, 1958, **48**, 1122.
147. N. CAGNOLI, *Farmaco (Pavia)*, ed. prat., 1958, **13**, 525.
148. L. L. HAWES, *Nature, (London)*, 1962, **196**, 766.
149. O. HASSEL and C. RØMMING, *Quart. Revs. (London)*, 1962, **16**, 1; O. HASSEL and J. HVOSLEF, *Acta Chem. Scand.*, 1954, **8**, 873; id. ibid., 1956, **10**, 138; O. HASSEL and C. RØMMING, ibid., 1956, **10**, 696; O. HASSEL and K. O. STRØMME, ibid., 1958, **12**, 1146; O. HASSEL, *Mol. Phys.*, 1958, **1**, 241; J. D. MCCULLOUGH *et al.*, *Acta Cryst.*, 1959, **12**, 815; L. J. ANDREWS and R. M. KEEFER, *Advances in Inorg. Chem. and Radiochem.*, ed. H. J. EMELÉUS and A. G. SHARPE, vol. 3, Acad. Press, New York, 1961, p. 127 *et seq.*
150. O. SCHMITZ-DUMONT and H. BORNEFIELD, *Z. anorg. allgem. Chem.*, 1956, **287**, 120.
151. S. GELLER and J. L. HOARD, *Acta Cryst.*, 1950, **3**, 121; J. L. HOARD *et al.*, ibid., 1950, **3**, 130; id. ibid., 1951, **4**, 396; S. GELLER and J. L. HOARD, ibid., 1951, **4**, 399; J. L. HOARD *et al.*, ibid., 1951, **4**, 405.
152. B. PESCE, *Gazzetta*, 1930, **60**, 936; J. L. HOARD and V. BLAIR, *J. Amer. Chem. Soc.*, 1935, **57**, 1985; L. J. KLINKENBERG and J. A. A. KETELAAR, *Rec. Trav. Chim.*, 1935, **54**, 959; L. J. KLINKENBERG, ibid., 1937, **56**, 36; R. W. G. WYCKHOFF, *Crystal Structures*, Interscience Publ., New York, 1951.
153. C. I. BRANDEN, *U.S. Dept. Com. Office Tech. Service*, AD 265, 316 (1961).
154. O. HASSEL and K. O. STRØMME, *Nature, (London)*, 1958, **182**, 1155.
155. S. C. WALLWORK and H. M. POWELL, *J. Chem. Soc.*, 1956, 4855.
156. S. I. SINGER and D. H. CAMPBELL, *J. Amer. Chem. Soc.*, 1953, **75**, 5577; S. I. SINGER *et al.*, ibid., 1955, **77**, 4855; id. ibid., 1959, **81**, 3887.
157. W. V. BHAGWAT and R. P. SHUKLA, *Agra Univ. J. Res.*, 1955, **4**, 1–4.
158. M. C. BAKER *et al.*, *J. Amer. Chem. Soc.*, 1956, **78**, 312; S. I. SINGER and D. H. CAMPBELL, ibid., 1955, **77**, 3499, 3504, 4851; L. G. LONGWORTH,

*Electrophoresis*, ed. M. BIER, Acad. Press, New York, 1959, pp. 91, 137.

159. T. UETA, *Scibutsu Butsuri Kagaku*, 1959, **6**, 41–49.

160. P. DEEKER, *Naturw.*, 1957, **44**, 305.

161. N. N. GREENWOOD *et al.*, *J. Chem. Soc.*, 1950, 3030.

162. D. D. DESHPANDE, *J. Univ. Poona, Sci. Tech.*, 1958, **14**, 55.

163. L. G. MELKONYAN *et al.*, *Referat. Zh. Khim.*, 1956, Abstr. No. 61034.

164. F. A. PEPE and S. I. SINGER, *J. Amer. Chem. Soc.*, 1959, **81**, 3878.

165. S. I. EPSTEIN *et al.*, *J. Amer. Chem. Soc.*, 1956, **78**, 3306; S. I. EPSTEIN and S. I. SINGER, ibid., 1958, **80**, 1274; P. DOTY and S. I. EPSTEIN, *Nature (London)*, 1954, **174**, 89.

166. P. P. SHORYGIN and A. KH. KHALILOV, *Zh. Fiz. Khim.*, 1951, **25**, 1475.

167. A. OTTENBERG *et al.*, *Nature (London)*, 1964, **201**, 1119.

168. R. S. MULLIKEN, *J. Phys. Chem.*, 1952, **56**, 801.

169. H. KAINER and W. OTTING, *Chem. Ber.*, 1955, **88**, 1921.

170. R. FOSTER and T. J. THOMSON, *Trans. Faraday Soc.*, 1963, **59**, 296.

171. J. V. HATTON and W. G. SCHNEIDER, *Can. J. Chem.*, 1962, **40**, 1285.

172. D. BIJL, *J. Chem. Phys.*, 1959, **30**, 765.

172a. G. P. KARPACHEVA, *Zh. Fiz. Khim.*, 1965, **39**, 3015.

172b. I. T. ERNST *et al.*, *J. Catalysis*, 1964, **3**, 568.

173. J. W. EASTMAN, *U.S. At. En. Comm.* UCRL–9722, 1961, p. 97.

174. F. P. CHERNYAKOVSKII *et al.*, *Zh. Fiz. Khim.*, 1962, **36**, 865.

175. E. CONSTANT and L. RACZY, *Compt. Rend.*, 1961, **253**, 2493.

176. M. M. LABES *et al.*, *J. Chem. Phys.*, 1960, **33**, 868; J. H. OSIECKI, *Nature, (London)*, 1963, **198**, 85.

177. D. B. CHESNUT and P. ARTHUR, *J. Chem. Phys.*, 1962, **36**, 2969; R. G. KEPLER, ibid., 1963, **39**, 3528.

178. S. S. BHATNAGAR and C. L. LAKRA, *Indian J. Phys.*, 1933, **8**, 43; S. R. RAO and S. R. GOVINDARAJAN, *Proc. Indian Acad. Sci.*, 1942, **15A**, 35; M. KONDO *et al.*, *Bull. Chem. Soc. Japan*, 1956, **29**, 305.

179. F. G. A. STONE, *Chem. Revs.*, 1958, **58**, 104.

180. H. C. BROWN *et al.*, *J. Amer. Chem. Soc.*, 1944, **66**, 431; H. C. BROWN and M. GERSTEIN, ibid., 1950, **73**, 2923.

181. H. C. BROWN and R. H. HOROWITZ, *J. Amer. Chem. Soc.*, 1955, **77**, 1730.

182. H. C. BROWN and D. GINTIS, *J. Amer. Chem. Soc.*, 1956, **78**, 5378.

183. H. C. BROWN and M. D. TAYLOR, *J. Amer. Chem. Soc.*, 1947, **69**, 1332; H. C. BROWN *et al.*, ibid., 1951, **73**, 2464; H. C. BROWN, *J. Chem Soc.*, 1956, 1248.

184. H. C. BROWN *et al.*, *Determination of Organic Structures by Physical Methods*, ed. E. A. BRAUDE and F. C. NACHOD, Acad. Press, New York, 1956, p. 567 *et seq.*

185. H. C. BROWN and H. PEARSALL, *J. Amer. Chem. Soc.*, 1945, **67**, 1765.

186. F. E. STEWART *et al.*, *J. Chem. Phys.*, 1966, **44**, 2866.

187. R. FOSTER and P. HANSON, *Tetrahedron*, 1965, **21**, 255.

188. S. CARTER *et al.*, *J. Chem. Soc.*, 1965, 2048.

189. G. D. JOHNSON and R. E. BOWEN, *J. Amer. Chem. Soc.*, 1965, **87**, 1655.

190. Y. MATSUNAGA, *Nature (London)*, 1966, **211**, 183.

191. M. E. BROWNE *et al.*, *J. Chem. Phys.*, 1964, **41**, 3265.

192. O. L. CARTER *et al.*, Private Communication (1966), to be published in the *J. Chem. Soc.*

193. D. S. BROWN and S. C. WALLWORK, *Acta Cryst.*, 1964, **17**, 168.

194. A. W. HANSON, *Acta Cryst.*, 1965, **19**, 19.

# CHAPTER 4

# PROPERTIES OF
# MOLECULAR COMPLEXES

THIS chapter is concerned with the results obtained by applying the methods outlined in Chapter 3 to the detailed study of physical properties of molecular complexes, viz. spectra, magetism, dipole moments, etc.

## 1. Spectra

The types of spectra of interest are electronic, infrared, Raman and luminescence spectra.

### (a) Electronic absorption spectra

The charge-transfer transition ($\Psi_E \leftarrow \Psi_N$) may be considered as causing an electron to jump from the donor $D$ to the acceptor $A$ molecule, since $a^2 \gg b^2$ in the wave equation [eqn. (2.1)]. This transition is thus characteristic of the complex, for it involves both $D$ and $A$, and it gives rise to an intense electronic spectrum. In general, the band shapes of the donor and acceptor moieties are greatly altered, while the variations in the vibration frequencies are considerable. This even occurs in the case of weak addition complexes, e.g. those formed between the halogen-acids and mixtures of benzene–carbon tetrachloride or benzene–phenol.[1] The moment ($\mu_{EN}$) associated with the charge-transfer transition depends on the average distances between the electrons in the orbitals of the donor and acceptor molecules and a conventional origin, and on the average position of an electron having a charge distribution of the form of the overlap of the wave functions of the two constituent species [see eqn. (2.7)].

In general, it appears that two conditions have to be satisfied for charge-transfer absorption to occur.[2,3]

(i) The donor shall have a high-energy filled orbital and the acceptor a low-energy vacant orbital.

(ii) The above orbitals shall overlap; this overlap may be sterically determined or derived either from chance collisions between the components or from complex formation.

With regard to the effect of the reaction medium on general charge-transfer absorption, it is possible to distinguish three types of acceptor–donor pairs[4] as follows:

(i) Between moieties of a neutral complex, e.g. unsaturated hydrocarbons reacting with nitro-compounds; in this case the electron transfer leads to an excited state more polar than the ground state, so that changing from a less to a more polar solvent brings about a red shift of the charge-transfer absorption; this effect is small, since the solvent molecules require a finite time to reorientate round the dipolar excited state. As a result of the reduction of the energy of the excited state by the solvent effect a frequency separation occurs between charge-transfer absorption and fluorescence bands of these complexes. Thus the frequency separation of the above bands for the hexamethylbenzene–tetrachlorophthalic anhydride complex increases with the refractivity and dielectric constant of the solvent.[5]

(ii) A reverse effect occurs in the case of an electron transfer between the components of an ion-pair. For instance, the charge-transfer band of 4-methoxycarbonylpyridine ethiodide moves from 448 Å in chloroform solution to 3311 Å in 7:3 ethanol–water solution[6] in this case the change of the charge-transfer transition with the dielectric constant of the solvent parallels closely the solvent shift of the $n \rightarrow \pi^*$ absorption ($n$ and $\pi^*$ are the non-bonding level and antibonding $\pi$ level), and the free energy of activation with solvent of reactions involving a redistribution of charge.

(iii) The third type of donor–acceptor pair is that involving a neutral and an ionic component, e.g. smaller non-metallic amines in polar solvents, or complexes of transition metals with neutral ligands. For example, the charge-transfer absorption of the iodide ion is shifted to slightly higher frequencies in hydroxylic solvents and to much lower frequencies in non-hydroxylic solvents, as the polarity of the solvent is reduced;[7] this absorption seems to depend to some extent on the electron affinity of the solvent molecules and, in solvents of low polarity, on specific cation effects.[8] Recent studies by Davis and Symons[123] indicate that for a large number of formally neutral charge-transfer complexes, an increase in solvent polarity does not result in a trend of the charge transfer band to lower frequencies, contrary to expectations. Indeed, a slight shift is observed towards higher frequencies. This behaviour is attributed to solvation; solvation forces are said to operate on separate constituents to give radical ions by a chemical reaction and not solvation of ion-pairs. It is postulated that solid complexes exist as neutral or ionic molecules, but not as mixtures of both.

The electronic spectrum of the molecular complexes may now be considered under four aspects, viz. polarization, intensity, energy and spectral position.

(i) *Polarization.* It is found that in the case of single crystals of complexes formed by reacting hexamethylbenzene with trinitrobenzene, in which the benzene rings are parallel, the absorption of light polarized in a direction perpendicular to the benzenoid planes is more intense than that polarized in the plane; the position of maximum absorption of the formed components is shifted to lower frequencies to a greater extent than that in the in-plane.[9] This effect is the reverse of that encountered in the non-complexed species (ref. 9, pp. 390 and 392). Indeed, it can be shown that the electron shift from the donor to the acceptor in the charge-transfer process can only be brought about by the light component which oscillates perpendicularly to the benzenoid rings.[10] Thus Nakamoto[9] has shown that the red colour of the solution containing chloranil and hexamethylbenzene is due primarily to the absorption of light which is polarized in a plane perpendicular to the planes of the aromatic rings (the moieties of the complex are stacked one upon the other in parallel planes); strong absorption of the separate components, on the other hand, takes place when the light is polarized in the plane of the aromatic rings.

(ii) *Intensity*. The theoretical oscillator strength may be evaluated by means of the equation

(4.1) $$f_t = 4 \cdot 704 \times 10^{-7} \bar{\nu}_{max} \mu_{EN}^2.$$

where $\mu_{EN}$ is the transition dipole moment associated with the $E \leftarrow N$ transition (a $E \leftarrow N$ or charge-transfer transition can be viewed as causing an electron to jump from the donor to the acceptor species since $a^2 \gg b^2$), and $\bar{\nu}_{max}$ is the wave number at the maximum of the absorption.[11] On the other hand, the observed oscillator strength $f_0$ is given by the expression

(4.2) $$f_0 = 1 \cdot 35 \times 10^{-8} \epsilon_{max} (\bar{\nu}_{max} - \bar{\nu}_{0 \cdot 5}),$$

where $\epsilon_{max}$ is the molar extinction coefficient at the absorption maximum, and $\bar{\nu}_{0 \cdot 5}$ is the half-width of the absorption band (S. P. McGlynn, loc. cit.). There is satisfactory agreement between the values of $f_t$ and $f_0$ in some cases.[2,12] It must be noted, however, that theory and experiment lead to different conclusions regarding the relation between $\mu_{EN}$, $f$ and $\epsilon$ on one hand, and the equilibrium constant $k$ of the complexes on the other. Theory predicts an increase of $\mu_{EN}$, $f$ and $\epsilon$ with increasing $k$, since $b$ increases with the enhanced resonance interaction [eqn. (2.1)]. The exact opposite is, however, the case,[13] i.e. the molar extinction coefficient at the absorption maximum decreases with the increasing donor character of the donor atom and acceptor character of the acceptor atom.[14] For example, the extinction coefficients of methylated benzene–iodine complexes decrease with the increasing methylation of the aromatic moiety. Indeed, the Mulliken prediction about the relationship between the intensity of the charge-transfer band and the stability of the complex is not supported by experiment, except perhaps in the case of chloranil or strong iodine–amine complexes.[15] A more general result is that the intensity of the band decreases as the stability of the complex increases.[15] It should also be noted that with certain exceptions the resonance energy $R_N$ of the complex also affects the value of the molar extinction coefficient at the absorption maximum,[15] viz.

$$\epsilon_{max} = 7 \cdot 7 \times 10^4 / \left( \frac{h\nu}{R_N} \right) - 3 \cdot 5.$$

In order to explain the above observations, especially in the case of the relation between $\epsilon_{max}$ and $k$, Mulliken developed the concept of contact charge-transfer,[16] (see Also L. E. Orgel and R. S. Mulliken,[3]). For instance, a solution of iodine in benzene is assumed to consist of a definite fraction of relatively favourably oriented but low-energy 1:1 complex molecules, close together, each of which is surrounded by non-interacting benzene molecules; in addition, the solution also contains some iodine molecules, which react at random with certain benzene molecules by forming loose charge-transfer contacts. In reality, of course, the solution will not contain these extremes, but a series of species ranging from loose contacts to stable entities. It seems that this hypothetical model leads to satisfactory agreement between experiments and theory, though certain discrepancies still exist;[3,17] these have been attributed to the effect of varying mixtures of orientation isomers,[3,14,16] deviations from ideality and contributions of contact charge-transfer spectra.[3,16,18]

Indirectly, the hypothesis of contact charge-transfer is supported by the observations that although gaseous iodine does not absorb at wavelengths greater than 200 m$\mu$ when dissolved in saturated hydrocarbons, it absorbs strongly up to 260 m$\mu$ (see also D. F. Evans, ref. 18). The same applies to solutions of oxygen[20] (see also D. F. Evans, ref. 18), bromine (D. F. Evans, ref. 18) and tetranitrobenzene[21] in benzene. Since there is no evidence for the existence of complexes of iodine and saturated hydrocarbons[19,22] (see also D. F. Evans, ref. 21), it is possible that absorption may be due to a charge-transfer transition during molecular collisions (D. F. Evans, ref. 21).

Recent evidence indicates that in certain complexes donor-excited states contribute the greatest intensity to charge-transfer bands, except when for reasons of symmetry they do not interact with the charge-transfer state.[23] Contact charge-transfer absorption is assumed to be due almost entirely to the interaction of charge-transfer with donor excited states. The intensity of the charge-transfer band may increase or decrease as the complex becomes more stable. These conclusions are derived from a study of solutions of the complexes of iodine or chloranil with various substituted aromatic hydrocarbons (carbon tetrachloride as a solvent for iodine, butyl ether for chloranil). For instance, in the case of complexes between methylbenzenes and iodine the charge-transfer intensity falls as the complex becomes more stable,[24] while the reverse is true for the methylbenzenes–chloranil complexes, i.e. the greater the stability, the larger the intensity of the charge-transfer band.[25] In general the relative intensities and stabilities in a series of related complexes depend on theoretical grounds on the variation of the difference in energy between the most stable configuration and that giving the greatest contribution to the intensity; those configurations are usually different, e.g. in the iodine–benzene series. In the methylbenzenes–iodine series, chance contacts are reduced as the stability of the complex increases, and hence the intensity of the charge-transfer band is reduced.[3] On the other hand, charge-transfer intensity in the methylbenzenes–chloranil complexes mainly arises from the interaction between the ground and charge-transfer state, since the geometry of the components makes it difficult to bring about much overlap between the accepting and donating orbitals, except when they lie one upon the other in parallel planes. In addition, no borrowing from the donor-excited state occurs in the case of the chloranil complexes, so that their charge-transfer intensity is very much less than that of the methylbenzenes–iodine complexes, for which the excited state of the donor contributes a large amount to the charge-transfer intensity. Table 4.1 shows the relevant values of the extinction coefficients $\epsilon$ and at wavelengths $\lambda$ of the stability constants $k$ of the complexes.[23,26]

TABLE 4.1. *Charge-transfer spectra of iodine (I) and chloranil (C) complexes*

| | Donors | | | | | | | | | | | | | |
|---|---|---|---|---|---|---|---|---|---|---|---|---|---|---|
| | Benzene | | Toluene | | o-Xylene | | 1,3,5-tri-methyl benzene | | 1,2,4,5,-tetra-methyl benzene | | Penta-methyl benzene | | Hexamethyl benzene | |
| Acceptors | I | C | I | C | I | C | I | C | I | C | I | C | I | C |
| $\lambda$(m$\mu$) | 292 | 340 | 302 | 365 | 316 | 385 | 332 | 410 | 332 | 470 | 357 | 480 | 375 | 505 |
| $\epsilon$ | 16400 | 2180 | 16700 | 1920 | 12500 | 2090 | 8850 | 2250 | 9000 | 2320 | 9260 | 2680 | 8200 | 2880 |
| $k$ | 0·15 | 0·30 | 0·16 | 0·50 | 0·27 | 1·05 | 0·82 | 1·17 | 0·63 | 3·02 | 0·88 | 5·32 | 1·35 | 9·08 |

Murrell[23] finds that the least symmetrical configuration, though the least stable, may give rise to the largest charge-transfer intensity. This is supported by the observation that the measured extinction coefficients of the charge-transfer bands of trinitrobenzene–naphthalene and trinitrobenzene–aniline complexes increase on heating the solution of the complexes, though fewer molecules are involved in complex formation and the net absorption decreases.[3]

Mason (ref. 4, p. 287) discusses the relative contributions of chance collisions and complexed donor–acceptor pairs from the point of view of mixing of the non-bonded $\Psi_0(D,A)$, and the ion-pair $\Psi_1(D^+ - A^-)$ wave functions; this mixing gives rise to a stabilized ground state function $\Psi_N$ and an excited state function $\Psi_E$, viz.

(4.3)        $\Psi_N = a\Psi_0(D,A) + b\Psi_1(D^+A^-),$

(4.4)        $\Psi_E = a^*\Psi_1((D^+ - A^-) - b^*\Psi_0(DA),$

where $a$ and $b$ are the mixing coefficients ($a \gg b$; $a^2 + b^2 = 1$), the values of which can be obtained from the heat of formation,[27] electronic spectrum,[19] or dipole moment[2] of the complex; the so-called charge-transfer band of the complex is then associated with the electronic transition $\Psi_N \rightarrow \Psi_E$. In the case of contact charge-transfer, i.e. statistical collision pairing, where no definite complex can be isolated, the orbitals of the components may overlap adequately to give the mixing described above, with an appreciable transition moment.[3] Thus for the iodine–benzene complex about three quarters of the observed charge-transfer intensity is derived from chance collisions;[3] the general tendency is thus for the absorption intensity of such complexes to decrease with the increasing stability constant.

A different situation arises, however, in the case of complexes of moderate strength, where complex charge-transfer contributes appreciably to the total observed absorption intensity. It may be shown theoretically[2] that in this instance the intensity of the charge-transfer absorption is proportional to the degree of mixing between the non-bonded $(D,A)$ and ion-pair $(D^+A^-)$ states. Hence the intensity will increase with the increase of the stability constant. This conclusion is supported by observations concerning the effect of pressure on charge-transfer spectra. For instance, at a pressure of 50,000 atm[28] the intensity of the absorption bond of the chloranil–hexamethylbenzene complex increases by a factor of 1·7, while its frequency is lowered by about 2500 cm$^{-1}$ (in general, the intensities of charge-transfer bands are inversely proportional to the wavelengths of absorption.[5]) The influence of pressure may be explained by considering the increase in repulsion between the outer shell electrons brought about by tremendous pressures; the energy interval between the non-bonded and ion-pair states will thus be reduced, so that a lower transition energy results with an attendant increase in mixing.

An additional source of charge-transfer absorption intensity is the probability of mixing of the charge-transfer transition with the transitions of the individual component molecules,[29] particularly those of the donor, as shown on pp. 89–90. This is not possible, however, when the donor and acceptor components are both aromatic, since the electron transfer occurs between the parallel aromatic rings. This view is supported by observations of polarized spectra of such complexes in the solid state, which appear to indicate that the charge-transfer transition moment is directed perpendicularly to the molecular planes.[9] Since the lower energy transitions of aromatic hydrocarbons are polarized in the molecular plane, they cannot mix with perpendicular transitions. On the other hand, there is a marked contribution by a donor transition to charge-transfer absorption in solution in the case of halogen–aromatic hydrocarbon complexes, where the above situation does not arise.[29,30] Similar considerations apply to complexes formed by sulphur dioxide with olefins,[31] and to the products of interaction of donor and acceptors having extended $\pi$-electron systems, e.g. hexamethylbenzene and tetracyanoethylene.[32] The problem of the donor-bond contribution is also considered on pp. 89–90.

*The effect of donor excited states.* The mathematical treatment of the effect of donor excited states in one-electron systems, in which the acceptor and donor are both neutral molecules, is given in some detail by Murrell;[33] for many-electron systems the derived equations have to be modified to some extent, though the essential terms have the same form.[23] The intensity of the charge-transfer spectrum is determined by the transition moment between the perturbed and charge-transfer state, which results from the interaction between the donor and the acceptor.[10] The equation cited by Murrell consists of two parts: one represents the contribution to the transition moment, which is proportional to the dipole moment of the transferred electron and the hole it leaves behind, the latter being itself proportional to the distance through which the charge is carried; the second part of the equation represents, according to Mulliken,[3] contact absorption, i.e. a spectrum appears, though no stable complex is formed, as, for example, in the case of iodine–heptane mixtures, when a spectrum appears at 260 m$\mu$ (*vide* D. F. Evans, ref. 18). In general, the first term is small, i.e. there is little stabilization in the ground state. As a result, a charge-transfer band will appear in the spectrum by virtue of the second part of the equation,[3] i.e. contact charge-transfer absorption will take place; this is the case when the ground and charge-transfer wave functions have different symmetries, so that the overlap density (the product of the two functions) lies far away from the acceptor moiety, but not too close to the donor component. Under these conditions a charge-transfer band polarized in a direction perpendicular to that of charge-transfer will appear in the spectrum of the inter-action products without any stabilization of the ground state. It is clear that a situation may arise when both terms are small, so that they contribute but little to the charge-transfer band. In other words, the second term of the equation may not be of importance in contact charge-transfer spectra.

In order to account for this particular situation, Murrell postulated that contact charge-transfer bands derive their intensity from the excited states of the donor or acceptor. For instance, if the donor has an intense absorption band, then some of it can be transferred to the charge-transfer band. This may be achieved by transferring an electron from an excited orbital of the donor to an excited orbital of the acceptor. The contact charge-transfer band may also derive its intensity from an excited state of the acceptor by transferring an electron from a ground state orbital of the donor to a ground state orbital of an acceptor.

The excited states of the donor and acceptor play a vital

role[23] in the case of weak complexes, which correspond to Mulliken's contact species. For instance, the iodine–benzene interaction gives rise to a large number of different configurations in solution, some of these being contact species. It is then possible that the donor and acceptor cannot contribute in the most stable configuration of the complex to the charge-transfer intensity for symmetry reasons.[30] In other words, the charge-transfer band of the complexes will gain no intensity from the donor or acceptor absorption bands in a symmetrical structure, though it will do so for the less stable contact configuration. For instance, the benzene absorption bands contribute to the charge-transfer intensity of the benzene–iodine complex when the symmetrical structure, involving a sixfold symmetry axis, is replaced by an unsymmetrical structure. Similarly, the donor absorption bands of quinones will not contribute to the spectral intensity of the quinone complexes, if the latter have a symmetrical sandwich structure.

It is evident from the above that for certain weak complexes displaying a number of configurations in solution, the charge-transfer intensity of a contact configuration may be greater than that of a complex. This explains why only in such cases the extinction coefficient increases as the stability of the complex decreases[3] and the temperature increases; the latter effect was found to be true in the case of some trinitrobenzene complexes.[3] On the other hand, the case of strong molecular complexes is rather different, since there the donor and acceptor states will contribute to the charge-transfer intensity, e.g. iodine–amine complexes.

(iii) *Energy.* The energy of a charge-transfer transition is given [see eqn. (2.3) *et seq.*] by the quantum mechanical relation

(4.5)
$$E = h\nu$$
$$= W_E - W_N,$$

where the $W$ terms refer to the energies associated with the relevant structures. By substituting the values for $W_E$ and $W_N$ from eqns. (2.3) and (2.4) and noting that for a small overlap $H_{01}$ will vary approximately as $S$, and $S$ as $S_{DA}$ (the $S$ terms are the overlaps), it is found that[16] the ground state energy $E$ associated with the total wave function of the complex is given by the relation

(4.6) $$E = I(D) - \delta + \frac{\{(d^*)^2 + d^2\}S_{DA}{}^2}{I(D) - \delta},$$

where $I(D)$ is the ionization potential of the donor $D$, $\delta$ is given approximately by $\delta \approx I_D - (W_1 - W_0)$, and $d$ and $d^*$ are factors such that $d^* > d$.
If one assumes the approximate constancy of the numerator in the above equation, one obtains

(4.7) $$E = I(D) - \gamma,$$

where $\gamma$ is a constant characteristic of the complex for a given acceptor $A$, i.e. the graph of $E$ against $I(D)$ is a straight line. This has been verified by experiment for polyacene–trinitro-benzene,[34] aromatic and heteroaromatic–dinitrobenzene,[12,27,35] and diverse aromatic–iodine complexes.[36] There is also a linear relationship between $I(D)$ and the frequency $\nu$ for complexes involving $p$–$\pi$ aromatic electron donors $(A)$ and $p$–$\pi$ electron acceptors $(D)$, where $D$ is, for example, hexamethylbenzene or $N$-methylaniline, while $A$ is $p$-benzoquinone or benzene. The corresponding equation is

(4.8) $$\nu = 0.85[I(D) - e],$$

where e is the apparent electron affinity.[37] Many deviations occur, however, especially in the case of weak donors, e.g. toluene (see below). It should also be noted that the linearity between $I(D)$ and $E$ has no good foundation in theory, since the parameter $\gamma$ should vary to the same extent, except in the case of very closely related donors.[16,34,38]

Another experimental linearity is that between the spectral transition energy at the band maximum and the wavelength. This phenomenon is observed when considering the effect of mixtures of solvents on the charge-transfer bonds of molecular complexes.[39] For instance, the charge-transfer band for 1-methyl-4-carbomethoxypyridinium iodide is sensitive to solvents, such as aqueous ethanol, methanol or acetone; the graph of the charge-transfer energy versus wavelength is linear, and the lines for various solvent mixtures converge on extrapolation to the same energy and wavelength values.

The problem of the relationship between the ionization potential of the donor and the charge-transfer band frequency has been reviewed in some detail by Briegleb[40] and critically by Mulliken.[41] They showed that for weak complexes the frequency $\nu_{CT}$ of the charge-transfer band is related to the vertical ionization potential of the isolated donor $I(D)^{\nu}$ by the relation

$$(4.9) \qquad h\nu_{CT} = I(D)^{\nu} - C_1 + \frac{C_2}{I(D)^{\nu} - C_1},$$

where $h$ is Planck's constant, and $C_1$ and $C_2$ are supposed to be constants for a given acceptor ($C_2$ is very small for weak complexes). It follows that when the energy $h\nu_{CT}$ is plotted against $I(D)$, a curve results similar to those given by the above equation, and $C_1$ and $C_2$ can then be evaluated. For example, for iodine as an acceptor $C_1$ and $C_2$ are 5·2 eV and 1·5 (eV)$^2$, respectively. However, the data for the iodine–pyridine and iodine–triethylamine complexes do not fit the curves given by eq. (4.9)[5] (also ref. 40, p. 78). These deviations may be partly due to the use of values of ionization energies $I(D)$ different from those of the *vertical* ionization energies;[42] furthermore, theory does not predict the constancy of $C_1$ and $C_2$ for a series of molecular complexes having the same acceptor moiety. Indeed, it can be shown experimentally that in certain cases the use of vertical ionization energies does not eliminate the deviations from linearity occurring for different complexes containing the same acceptor, e.g. iodine–amine complexes.[43] In the latter case the pertubation theory leads to a much more complex equation, the graphical solution of which yields values of $C_1$ and $C_2$ quite different from those relating to other iodine complexes. This divergence is probably due to the fact that in the iodine–amine complexes (*n*-donor–$\sigma$-acceptor) the two moieties approach each other more closely than those in the looser $\pi$-complexes. Though both equations imply a lack of linearity between $h\nu_{CT}$ and $I(D)$, the actual graphs are only slightly curved, but the slopes are less than unity[36,37] owing to non-zero resonance interaction. In general, the slopes fall increasingly below unity for increasingly strong complexes, while approaching unity for weak complexes

(iv) *Spectral position.* Certain molecular complexes give, however, electronic spectra situated entirely in the ultraviolet region.[32] Thus tetrahydrophthalic anhydride and anthracene, tetrahydrophthalic anhydride and hexamethylbenzene, and 1,3,5-trinitrobenzene and anthracene give in dilute solution at −180°C ultraviolet electronic spectra which show a loss of fine structure, some frequency shifts and little change in the intensities in the bands. The symmetry-forbidden longest wavelength band of the system iodine–hexamethylbenzene is shifted greatly to the red and its intensity is increased tenfold, so that nearly all forbiddenness is removed. In general, perturbation of spectra can be discussed in terms of complex formation.[44] The correctness of numerical data concerning photo-scatter spectra and relaxation times of aromatic hydrocarbons in donor–acceptor complexes has been investigated by Czekalla.[32]

The visible and ultraviolet spectra of molecular complexes involving organic moieties have been studied on the basis of Mulliken's assumption[2] that photochemical charge-transfer is responsible for the light absorption.[5,45] The frequency of a photon, $\nu_{CT}$, needed to effect the charge-transfer is given approximately by the relation

$$(4.10) \qquad \nu_{CT} = I(D) - E(A) - \Delta,$$

where $E(A)$ is the electron affinity of the acceptor, and $\Delta$ is an approximate constant (ref. 4, p. 287) for a given series of compounds (in effect, $\Delta$ is the difference between the binding energies of the components in the ground and the excited state); this energy term $\Delta$ does, however, vary with the nature of the components of the complex. In general, electron donors of low ionization potential form charge-transfer complexes with acceptors of high electron affinity. In these cases the charge-transfer absorption bands are shifted to longer wavelengths relative to those of the components.[46] The systems studied were those involving chloranil, bromanil or iodanil as acceptors, and aniline or N-methylaniline as donors. Equation (4.10) leads to the following conclusions:

(a) For a particular donor, the frequency of the charge-transfer absorption band is proportional to the electron affinity of the acceptor in a given series of complexes.[47]

(b) For a given acceptor, the frequency of the charge-transfer band is proportional to the ionization potential of the donor in a given series of complexes.[15,36]

It may be shown, however, by experiment that the value of $\Delta\nu/\Delta I(D)$ is less than unity in many cases†, e.g. complex formation between tetracyanoethylene and a series of methylbenzenes leads[48] to a value of 0·49 for the above ratio, while 0·67 is the value of the ratio in the case of iodine and aromatic or olefinic donors.[36] On the other hand, the use of the theoretical ionization energies of the highest-occupied $\pi$-electron orbital leads to the ratio $\Delta\nu/\Delta I(D)$ of nearly unity in the case of unsubstituted polycyclic aromatic hydrocarbon donors; in this case the steric effects, which are important in other instances,[30,49] affect but slightly the relation between the frequency and the ionization potential of the donor moiety.

Another relation postulated for the energy of charge-transfer absorption bands is that between the absorption maximum and the factor $P$ of the donor;[50] the $P$ factor is a measure of the energy of an electron in the highest filled orbital. This relation has been found to be linear for complexes having an absorption maximum in the near infrared spectrum, especially those of biological importance.

Investigation of the positions of the absorption bands of organic charge-transfer complexes has resulted in certain empirical regularities being observed. Thus the frequencies of the bands of chloranil[51] or iodine[36] charge-transfer complexes are proportional to those of the lowest singlet absorption of the donor molecule. For the acceptors chloranil or trinitrobenzene the widths of the absorption bands at half-maximum extinction are proportional to the frequencies of maximum absorption[5] so that larger transition energy denotes a greater difference between the ground and excited state dimensions.

## (b) Infrared and Raman spectra

The donor–acceptor interaction, which is associated with a

---

†$\Delta$ in this fraction is not the energy term $\Delta$ above but a difference symbol.

partial removal of electrons from the bonding orbitals of the donor $D$ to the antibonding orbitals of the acceptor $A$, brings about the following effects:

(i)  The bond length between certain atoms in the acceptor and donor molecules increases. For example, in the acceptor iodine the bond distance in the molecule $I_2$ increases from 2·67 to 2·90 Å when dissolved in pyridine.[52]

(ii)  The extinction coefficients[53] of the maximum of the infrared bands of solutions are generally enhanced in charge-transfer transitions owing to a change in the vertical ionization energy or vertical electron affinity during molecular vibrations, as in the benzene–iodine complex. It is worth noting that it is possible to calculate the ionization potentials of donors from the spectra of complexes,[54] the acceptors investigated being iodine, chloranil, trinitrobenzene and aromatic hydrocarbons.

(iii)  The vibration frequencies of the donor molecule decrease on complex formation, since the force constants of certain modes are sensitive to active orbitals involved in charge-transfer interactions, especially if the molecules are small and have more localized active orbitals. For instance, in the olefine–silver ion complex[55] there is a decrease of about 65 cm$^{-1}$ in the ethylenic $C=C$ stretching frequency from that in an isolated olefin molecule. This decrease is quite considerable because of the localized nature of $\pi$-electrons in non-conjugated ethylenic species. On the other hand, the shift in the case of the benzene–silver ion complex is small because of the reduced localization of the relevant electrons.

As far as the frequency shifts of the acceptor species are concerned, considerable decreases in the vibration frequencies have been observed. Thus the fundamental vibration frequency of chlorine decreases from 557 cm$^{-1}$ in the "free" state of 526 cm$^{-1}$ when dissolved in benzene;[56] this effect is smaller in the case of the bromine–benzene interaction owing to the weaker acceptor nature of the bromine.[57] For the iodine–chloride acceptor interacting with various donors the vibration frequency of the interhalogen compound decreases with the increasing value of the equilibrium constant of the complex, i.e. with increasing charge-transfer.[58]

(iv) Since the total symmetry decreases on complex formation the hitherto forbidden transitions on symmetry grounds will give rise to new bands. For instance,[59] two enhanced bands appear in the case of the benzene–iodine complex at 992 and 850 cm$^{-1}$; this effect is not observed in the case of the vibration spectra of the saturated hydrocarbons–halogens systems.[60]

An interesting case is that concerning the spectral band of chlorine at 557 cm$^{-1}$. This bond is only Raman-active, but it appears in the infrared spectrum at 526 cm$^{-1}$ for the chlorine–benzene system, probably due to the unsymmetrical geometry. The results obtained in this particular case are at variance with those derived by means of the overlap principles. This discrepancy is explained (ref. 18) by assuming that a chlorine molecule is in contact with several benzene molecules. Hence, although two chlorine atoms are interacting in an equivalent fashion with one benzene molecule they do not do so with one another, and hence there is a resultant dipole moment in the chlorine molecule and infrared absorption occurs.

The infrared spectra of a large number of molecular complexes have been investigated in detail[61] especially those of the halides of the elements Al$^{III}$, Sn$^{IV}$, Ti$^{IV}$ and Fe$^{III}$ with compounds acting as donors, e.g. nitric oxide, pyridine, acetonitrile, acetone, ether, ethyl acetate and alcohol.[62] There is, as expected, a frequency shift in the infrared spectrum on complex formation. For example the 1876 cm$^{-1}$ frequency of nitric oxide is shifted to 2142 cm$^{-1}$ during the interaction with aluminium bromide because of the formation of partially ionized nitric oxide N $\vdots$ O$^+$; there is, however, a decrease of the O $-$ H and C $-$ O bond frequencies, though the C $-$ H bond frequency in ketones, esters and alcohols increases.[63] Sometimes a band disappears and a new band makes its appearance, e.g. the 1745 and 1250 cm$^{-1}$ bands of ethyl acetate disappear when this ester combines with aluminium halides owing to the interaction with the carbonyl group. For the pyridine donor the frequency shift increases with the acidity of the metal halides, the latter behaving like strong acids.

Another example is that of the addition complex formed

between boron trifluoride and acetone or di-$n$-propylketone. The infrared spectra of the solid complexes and their solutions in benzene show a $C-O$ frequency shift from $1710$ cm$^{-1}$ in the free state to $1635-1640$ cm$^{-1}$ in the complex.[64] At the same time the dipole moment increases from $2.64D$ for the ketone to $6.59D$ for the complex. This points to the formation of a covalent $B-O$ bond and a weakening of the $C-O$ bond. The Raman and infrared spectra of molecular complexes formed by Lewis acids and bases have been described in detail;[65] the observed frequencies have been assigned and the regularities observed have been found to be similar to those in aromatic compounds with electronegative substituents.

A rather more complex case is that of the iodine–pyridine complex in benzene.[66] The equilibrium vibration frequency of iodine is shifted on complex formation from $213$ to $174$ cm$^{-1}$, while a weak band appears at $204$ cm$^{-1}$; the latter does not appear in $n$-heptane solutions of the complex. The bands at $174$ and $204$ cm$^{-1}$ are ascribed to the pyridine–iodine and benzene–iodine complexes, respectively; the $204$ cm$^{-1}$ band is possibly a contact spectrum (see p. 89).

The infrared spectra of molecular complexes have been reviewed at length by Briegleb,[40] while more recent work is concerned with the complexes of pyridine and bipyridines,[67] methylated benzenes,[68] trihalide ions,[66] halogens,[70] and also with the relevant theoretical discussion.[41,71] Mulliken and Person[41] have made some cogent and critical comments concerning the theory of infrared spectra. Firstly, the changes in force constants $\Delta k$ and effective charge $\Delta(d\mu/dr)$, which can be calculated from frequency and intensity changes in absorption bands, appear to exhibit similar behaviour in a large number of complexes[58,71,72] from the point of view of the $X-Y$ stretching vibration in $D \ldots X-Y$ complexes. For instance, small changes in $k$ and $d\mu/dr$ may bring about extensive changes in the spectra of the donor molecule of the complex and profoundly alter its appearance, e.g. pyridine;[71,73] the reverse is true for the halogen complexes.[41] It must be noted, however, that an extensive change in the appearance of the spectrum may be brought about without a large change in $k$ by a change of symmetry on complex formation.

Secondly, various attempts have been made to explain the intensification of the $X - Y$ stretching vibration in $D \ldots X - Y$ charge-transfer complexes. The concept of the polarization of the $X - Y$ bond by the negative charge of the active atom of the donor, which results in an added effective charge and thus in increased intensity,[58] has been disproved by Ferguson and Matsen;[70] they showed this effect could only account for an increase of 10% of the observed intensification. For halogen and hydrogen-bonded complexes the intensification of the $X - Y$ stretching vibration appears to be due to the varying contribution of the dative structure as the $X - Y$ bond length oscillates; there is thus an oscillating flow of electrons from donor to acceptor with the frequency of the $X - Y$ stretching vibration[41,53,70] (see also H. B. Friedrich, and W. D. Jones and W. T. Simpson, ref. 71).

### (c) Luminescence spectra

A solid glassy solution of trinitrobenzene and anthracene yields on irradiation with light of an appropriate wavelength an emission spectrum[74] which does not resemble the known $T \longrightarrow S$ emission of the hydrocarbon donor.[34,58,75] There is,[35,76] however, a mirror-image relationship between the emission spectrum, i.e. luminescence, and the charge-transfer absorption bands $E \longleftarrow N$. This conclusion is supported by the observation that in complexes of the same donor with a series of acceptors, for which the electron affinity increases, the charge-transfer absorption and luminescence both move to lower frequencies, thus preserving the mirror-image relationship.[76] It is to be noted, however, that the luminescence of the anthracene–trinitrobenzene complex is very similar to the phosphorescence spectrum $(T \longrightarrow S)$ of the free donor anthracene. Furthermore, one of the two observable electronic transitions in the emission spectrum of solid solutions of the anthracene–sym. trinitrobenzene system in ether–isopentane glass at 77°K is the $T \longrightarrow S$ phosphorescence which is largely localized on the hydrocarbon component.[77] This is similar to the $T \longrightarrow S$ emission of anthracene itself but blue-shifted by 113 cm$^{-1}$; there is also a half-decrease in the life-time of the phosphorescence and a decrease of the ground state vibration frequency.

On closer inspection of the spectrum of the anthracene-trinitrobenzene complex it may be seen that the observed single emission band[11] consists of two parts: a weak part corresponding to the $T \longrightarrow S$ transition of the free donor, and a strong component that is a good mirror-image of the $E \longleftarrow N$ absorption and has a normal fluorescent life-time. Moreover, the $E \longrightarrow N$ fluorescence is generally structureless, and hence the vibration characteristics of the phosphorescence determine the structure of the total emission; the similarity between the luminescence $(E \longrightarrow N)$ (reverse of charge-transfer absorption) and, phosphorescence $(T \longrightarrow S)$ is thus explained. The coincidence of both spectra in many trinitrobenzene complexes is due to an approximate constancy of the difference in energy of the vertical ionization potential and the lowest triplet of many aromatic hydrocarbons. In other complexes this constancy may not occur, so that there will be a large spectral separation between the two emission bonds, e.g. complexes of tetrachlorophthalic anhydride with anthracene or other aromatic hydrocarbons.[78]

A rather more elaborate explanation is based on the charge-transfer concept.[34] It is assumed that two processes are involved: in the first stage $E \longleftarrow N$ absorption occurs; this is followed by the $E \longrightarrow N$ fluorescence, as well as by a nearly simultaneous process in which energy is transferred from the mainly ionic $^1E$ state to a lower-energy triplet state $^3N^*$. This energy transfer will occur near the crossing of the $^1E$ and $^3N^*$ curves. Furthermore, since the $^3N^*$ state is dissociative at the crossing point of the curves, the complex will dissociate to a considerable extent to yield the acceptor molecule in its ground state and the donor species in its lowest excited triplet $^3B_{2u}$ state. Finally, the donor molecule will return to its ground state by the $T \longrightarrow S$ phosphorescence transition, this phosphorescence being much more intense than that of the uncomplexed donor. The above mechanism will operate, provided that the lowest level of the triplet state of the donor is energetically lower than the first excited charge-transfer state of the complex. This is valid for complexes formed between aromatic hydrocarbons and trinitrobenzene.

In connection with the $T \longleftarrow S$ transitions it is worth noting[79] that the $(T \leftarrow S)$ absorption bands characteristic of molecular complexes are diffuse, show little resolution and display a very high value of the molar extinction coefficient ($\epsilon_{max}$) at the absorption maximum, while the corresponding bands of the aromatic donors are well resolved and sharp and have a much lower coefficient $\epsilon_{max}$. This and other evidence suggests that the absorption bands of the charge-transfer complexes are not enhanced bands of the donor, but are due to the slight extent of the penetration of the donor $\pi$-electrons into the field of heavy atoms of the acceptor; the greater the atomic number of the acceptor atom, the smaller the penetration and thus the greater the oscillator strength of the $T \leftarrow S$ absorption of the molecules. Hence on mixing two colourless liquids of the donor $\alpha$-chloronaphthalene and acceptor ethyl iodide a deep yellow colour appears immediately. This interpretation does, of course, imply charge-transfer, and the diffuseness of the absorption bonds is in accord with the charge-transfer theory.[36]

The problem of intermolecular energy transfer in chemiluminescent reactions has been studied by Vassil'ev.[80] The excited product of the reaction is the donor (a ketone), while anthracene acts as an acceptor (activator). The activated chemiluminescent spectrum is a fluorescent spectrum of the acceptor and hence the singlet state of the activator is excited. It is possible to calculate the transfer constant from the relation between chemiluminescent intensity and the concentration of the activator, and it is found that on introducing more halogen atoms into the activator molecule and thus increasing its molecular weight, this constant increases. This observation indicates spin-coupling in the activator molecule. Furthermore, it is believed that the energy transfer occurs by an exchange of electrons between the donor and acceptor in a state of diffusion-controlled collision and not by exchange-resonance transfer.

## 2. Magnetic susceptibility

Pascal's law of additivity of magnetic susceptibilities ($\chi_M$) does not, in general, apply to the formation of molecular complexes. For instance, $\chi_M$ of the benzene–iodine complex is less than the sum of the separate values of $\chi_M$ of the two constituents,[81] i.e. benzene solutions of iodine are more diamagnetic than predicted. Similar considerations apply to the system polyacene-trinitrobenzene,[82] the increase being greatest for anthracene in the order anthracene > phenanthrene > naphthalene; this order follows that of stabilities and donor–acceptor resonance interaction.[34] Indeed, the increasing delocalization of electrons affects diamagnetism in accordance with eqn. (2.1), when $c = 0$ and $a \rightarrow b$. On the other hand, a different picture presents itself in the case of primarily ionic complexes, e.g. that of phenyl-enediamine with $p$-benzoquinone[83] in which there is, in addition to a singlet ground state, a well-stabilized triplet state at a slightly higher energy, so that the complex is paramagnetic and the dative-bond structure is represented by two wave functions. In fact this complex is nearly a diradical and it is termed a di-radicaloid.[83] If, however, the dative-bond structure is largely stabilized as in the case of $Et_3N \rightarrow BF_3 \cdot NH_3$ complex, the substance is not paramagnetic. In general, the triplet is low if there is a sufficiently large difference in the redox potentials of the donor and acceptor, and if there is only a small overlap of the charge clouds of unpaired electrons, as, for example, in the case of the Schlenk complexes of aromatic diamines and quinones. The susceptibilities $\chi_M$ at 90°K calculated from paramagnetic resonance[84] and the redox potentials are shown in Table 4.2. The corresponding values of $\chi_M$ for the same benzoquinones and $N,N\text{-}N',N'$-tetramethyl-$p$-phenylenediamine are 0·1, 0·2, 2·0 and 20 respectively. This is also observed with complexes of the

TABLE 4.2. *Redox potentials and magnetic susceptibilities of p-phenylenediamine–A complexes*

| Acceptor ($A$) | Redox potential (volt) | Magnetic susceptibility ($\chi_M$) |
|---|---|---|
| $p$-benzoquinone | 0·771 | Diamagnetic |
| tetrachloro-$p$-benzoquinone | 0·742 | 0·15 |
| tetrabromo-$p$-benzoquinone | 0·742 | 0·30 |
| tetraiodo-$p$-benzoquinone | — | 7·0 |

above substituted diamines with other quinones, when there is a considerable increase of $\chi_M$ of the complex, as the redox potentials of the quinones increase. At the same time the complexes exhibit a blue–red colour in polar solvents, though they are colourless in non-polar solvents.

Other polycyclic aromatic hydrocarbons, e.g. perylene yield molecular complexes with reduced diamagnetism;[85] these complexes have low resistivity, the large conductance being mainly electronic in nature.[86] The hydrocarbons themselves are, of course, semiconductors, since the energy gap for conductance is similar to the excitation energy of the triplet state.[87] In order to interpret this behaviour it is assumed that in diradicaloids the energy of the triplet state relative to the ground state decreases on complex formation, so that both the magnetic susceptibility and electrical conductance change. Another possible cause is the extensive orbital delocalization in macromolecular lattices. In addition there exist complexes for which the contribution of the triplet state to paramagnetism is not clear, e.g. 4,4'-dimethoxybiphenyl and its derivatives, which show electron spin resonance.[88]

### 3. Dipole moments

The dipole moment $\mu_M$ of a molecular complex is given by the relation

$$(4.11) \qquad \mu_M = -e \int \Psi_N \sum_i r_i \Psi_N d\tau,$$

where $e$ is the electronic charge and $r_i$ the vector distance of the $i$th electron from any suitable origin. If both the donor and acceptor species are non-polar, the dipole moment $\mu_{DA}$, which is associated with the dative-bond structure $(D \rightarrow A)$ is related to the dipole moment of the complex by the equation

$$(4.12) \qquad \mu_M = \mu_{DA} (b^2 + abS)$$

This follows from eqn. (2.1) *et seq.*[2, 12, 89, 90] If, however, the moment of the no-bond structure is not zero, eqns. (2.1) and (2.4) lead to the following expressions[2]

$$a^*(b + aS) = b^*(bS + a)$$

and

$$a^2 + 2abS + b^2 = a^{*2} - 2a^*b^*S = 1$$

(the terms have the same meaning as on pp. 12–14, Chapter 2; $\pi_M$, with the implied restrictions, is approximately equal to $er_M$, where $r_M$ is the equilibrium separation of the two components). Hence if the values of $S$, $\mu_M$ and $\mu_{DA}$ are found, then those of $a$, $b$, $a^*$ and $b^*$ can be calculated from the above equation. In addition the percentage ionic character of the ground state $I$, which is given by:

$$(4.13) \qquad I = \frac{100\,b^2}{a^2 + b^2}$$

can also be found. Some of these values are shown in Table 4.3.

TABLE 4.3. *Ionic character of bonds and dipole moments*

| Complex | $S$ | $a$ | $b$ | $a^*$ | $b^*$ | $I$ | Ref. |
|---|---|---|---|---|---|---|---|
| Durene–trinitrobenzene | 0·55 | 0·975 | 0·145 | 0·994 | 0·244 | 2·1 | 12 |
| Hexamethylbenzene–chloranil | 1·00 | 0·957 | 0·209 | 0·983 | 0·306 | 4·4 | 12 |
| Benzene–iodine | 1·80 | 0·93 | 0·286 | 0·964 | 0·381 | 8·2 | 12 and 90 |
| Pyridine–iodine | 4·5 | 0·86 | 0·50 | — | — | 25 | 91 |

It is seen that $a$ and $b$ are small but the contribution of the dative bond to the binding energy of the complex is large, because of the large binding energy of the dative-bond structure (that for the no-bond structure is negligible). Thus[12] for the durene–trinitrobenzene structure the relevant contribution is 47%, while that for the benzene–iodine complex[2, 91] is nearly 100%.

If one of the constituents of the complex has an initial dipole moment $\mu$, then there will be, in general, a difference between the dipole moments of the complex and its constituent moieties.

For instance, the dipole moment of nitrobenzene ($4\cdot22D$) is reduced to $3\cdot73\,D$ in the nitrobenzene–naphthalene complex; the corresponding figures for $m$-dinitrobenzene are $3\cdot79$ and $3\cdot43D$ respectively. In the case of the complexes formed between aromatic nitrocompounds and aluminium bromide[92] which dissolve in carbon disulphide, the change in dipole moments indicates addition to the nitro groups. On the other hand,[90, 93, 94] while the dipole moment of pyridine is $2\cdot28D$ that of the complex pyridine–iodine is $4\cdot5\,D$; this increase is due to the large mesomeric moment of the complex. Similar behaviour is shown by the benzene–chromium tricarbonyl and the cyclo-pentadienyl metal compounds (Fe, Ni, Mn, Cr, V, Sn, Pb, Mg and Be) when dissolved in heptane, benzene or dioxane. It is found that the values of the dipole moments of the compounds with polar metal-ring bonds are much greater in dioxane than in other solvents, because of donor-acceptor interaction.[95]

Finally, the calculation of bond moments in molecular complexes is based on numerous assumptions which must be made. For instance, in the case of boron trifluoride complexes it is essential to make the following assumptions: (1) boron trifluoride,[96] originally planar and with zero dipole moment, becomes tetrahedral in complexes and thus contributes to the total moment; the extent of this contribution is assumed to be $1\cdot5D$;[96] (2) it is supposed that the dipole moment of the donor remains unchanged during complex formation; (3) it is assumed that the total dipole moment of the complex is equal to that of all the bond moments, so that the contribution of the lone pairs to the total moment is unjustifiably ignored.[97]

## 4. Other physical properties

Boron trifluoride forms a large number of molecular complexes with all degrees of stability. In view of the unusual valency problems they pose, and their remarkable catalytic activity in organic reactions, the physical properties of the boron trifluoride complexes have received a great deal of attention.[98] The conclusions reached by these authors are as follows:

(i) *Molar refraction.* This physical property[99] of boron trifluoride is given as $6\cdot09$, so that the difference ($\Delta R$) between the molar refraction of the molecular complex and that of the donor moiety should be about 6, provided that this function were additive. In fact, this has not been observed, even after making allowances for partial decomposition.[100] On the other hand, certain regularities have been observed in some series, e.g. for dialcoholates $\Delta R$ is about 2·6, while for fatty acids $\Delta R$ is about 5·5.

(ii) *Viscosity.* The study of the viscosities of molten boron trifluoride complexes at various temperatures[101] indicates that either Batschinski's equation ($v = b + B/\eta$) or an exponential relation ($\eta = \eta_0 e^{E\eta/RT}$) may represent the temperature variation of the viscosity $\eta$ ($\eta_0$, $b$ and $B$ are constants, $v$ is the specific volume, and $E_\eta$ is the activation energy of viscous flow). It has been found that with very few exceptions the viscosity and the activation energy of viscous flow of the complex are considerably greater than those of the donor. It is also interesting to note that the viscosity of a 1 : 1 complex is larger than that of the corresponding 1 : 2 complex, e.g. the values of $\eta$ (cp) for $BF_3 \cdot MeOH$ and $BF_3 \cdot 2MeOH$ are 2·77 and 2·50 respectively, while in a homologous series the viscosity increases with chain length, e.g. the corresponding values of $\eta$ (cp) for $BF_3 \cdot 2EtOH$ and $BF_3 \cdot 2$ PrOH($n$) are 3·06 and 5·21, respectively.

(iii) *Surface tension.* Complex formation involves a large increase in the numerical magnitude of the surface tensions ($\gamma$) of the moieties, but the temperature coefficient decreases at the same time.[102] The parachor determinations have not been found to be useful in this field (Parachor $[P] = V_M \gamma^{1/4}$, where $V_M$ is the molar volume), for it has been established that parachor values do not decrease significantly during complex formation.[103]

A related property is the molar free energy $\omega$ given by the relation

(4.14) $$\omega = \gamma(V_M)^{2/3} = \omega_0 - kt,$$

where $k$ is the Eötvös constant, $t$ is the temperature and $\omega_0$ is equal to $kt$ when the free energy is zero, i.e. when the meniscus vanishes at the critical temperature. It is to be noted, however, that linear extrapolation beyond the experimental range for the purpose of finding the critical temperatures of boron trifluoride complexes is misleading (A. W. Laubengayer and G. R. Finlay, ref. 102).

(iv) *Electrical conductivity.* It is frequently found that the specific electrical conductivity $\kappa$ of molten complexes of boron trifluoride is very large approaching that of molten salts or solutions of strong electrolytes[104] (see also N. N. Greenwood *et al.*, and N. N. Greenwood and R. L. Martin, ref. 101); the specific conductivity of liquid $BF_3$ itself is negligible (*ca.* $5 \times 10^{-10}$ mhos/cm, while those of the free donor liquids are about $10^{-6}$ mhos/cm[105]). Thus, while the specific conductivity of saturated aqueous solution of sodium chloride at 25°C is 0·25 mhos/cm, that of the complex $BF_3 \cdot MeOH$ is 0·124 mhos/cm at the same temperature. This points to a high degree of ionic dissociation in the molten state. Further support for this observation is supplied by the examination of the values of molar conductivities ($\Lambda_M = M\kappa/d$, where $M$ is the molecular weight and $d$ is the density of the liquid complex) and "reduced" conductivities $\Lambda_R$ ($\Lambda_R = M\kappa\eta/d$, defined as the conductivity of one mole of complex reduced to a standard of one centipoise). The molar conductivities of the alcoholates and inorganic complexes of boron trifluoride are of the order of unity, while those for ester complexes are of the order of $10^{-2}$ mhos/cm. The values of the "reduced" conductivities range from $3·92 \times 10^{-2}$ mhos cm² cp for the $BF_3 \cdot MeCO_2$ Bu($n$) complex to the very high value of about 105 mhos cm² cp for $(BF_3)_2 \cdot H_4P_2O_7$. In general the values are about unity. Since values of $\Lambda_R$ are numerically equal to the degree of ionic dissociation, provided that the complex is a univalent electrolytic, it is clear that many of these complexes are highly dissociated in the molten ·state. It is also to be noted that the high conductivities of the molten complexes and the presence of the minima at stoichiometric ratios support the view that the high conductivities are *not* due to electrolytic impurities.[106] Table 4.4 shows the relevant data.

It should be noted that the modes of dissociation shown in Table 4.4 refer to pure liquids and do not necessarily represent the behaviour of complexes in various organic solvents where the ionic environment is quite different.[108]

On studying the slope of the curve of $\log \kappa$ versus $1/T$ one notes that the activation energy of ionic migration shows no

TABLE 4.4. *Electrical properties of boron-trifluoride complexes*

| Complex | $\kappa$ (mhos/cm) | $\Lambda_M$ (mhos cm$^2$) | $\Lambda_R$ (mhos cm$^2$ cp) | Mode of ionization | Degree of ionization | Ref. |
|---|---|---|---|---|---|---|
| BF$_3 \cdot$ H$_2$O | $1 \cdot 82 \times 10^{-2}$ | $8 \cdot 71 \times 10^{-1}$ | $10 \cdot 4$ | H$^+$ + BF$_3$OH$^-$ | 10 | 101 (N. N. Greenwood and R. L. Martin, p. 1915) 106 |
| BF$_3 \cdot$ 2H$_2$O | $5 \cdot 82 \times 10^{-2}$ | $3 \cdot 67$ | $18 \cdot 7$ | H$_3$O$^+$ + BF$_3$OH$^-$ | 20 | 101 (N. N. Greenwood and R. L. Martin, p. 1915) 106 |
| BF$_3 \cdot$ MeOH | $1 \cdot 24 \times 10^{-2}$ | $8 \cdot 83 \times 10^{-1}$ | $2 \cdot 22$ | H$^+$ + BF$_3$OMe$^-$ | 2 | 101 (N. N. Greenwood and R. L. Martin, p. 757) 106 |
| BF$_3 \cdot$ 2MeOH | $2 \cdot 95 \times 10^{-2}$ | $3 \cdot 22$ | $7 \cdot 34$ | MeOH$_2^+$ + BF$_3$OMe$^-$ | 7 | 101 (N. N. Greenwood and R. L. Martin, p. 757) 106 |
| BF$_3 \cdot$ 2PrOH($n$) | $3 \cdot 8 \times 10^{-3}$ | $6 \cdot 8 \times 10^{-1}$ | $3 \cdot 10$ | Pr($n$)OH$_2^+$ + BF$_3$OPr$^-$ ($n$) | 3 | 98 (pp. 13 and 26) 106 |
| BF$_3 \cdot$ MeCO$_2$H | $2 \cdot 41 \times 10^{-3}$ | $2 \cdot 10 \times 10^{-1}$ | $4 \cdot 67$ | H$^+$ + BF$_3 \cdot$ MeCO$_2^-$ | 5 | 106 107 |
| BF$_3 \cdot$ MeCO$_2$Me | $7 \cdot 70 \times 10^{-4}$ | $8 \cdot 80 \times 10^{-2}$ | $0 \cdot 18$ | H$^+$ + BF$_3$MeCO$_2$CH$_2^-$ and MeCO$^+$ + BF$_3$OMe$^-$ | 0·2 | 98 (pp. 13 and 26) |
| BF$_3 \cdot$ MeCO$_2$Et | $1 \cdot 82 \times 10^{-2}$ | $2 \cdot 30 \times 10^{-2}$ | $0 \cdot 0958$ | H$^+$ + BF$_3$MeCO$_2$C$_2$H$_4^-$ and MeCO$^+$ + BF$_3$O Et$^-$ | 0·09 | 106 98 (p. 13) 106 |

systematic variation in a homologous series. However, this energy is very similar to the corresponding activation energy of viscous flow $E_\eta$, so that mobility effects rather than changes in the degree of ionic dissociation are probably the main facts influencing the behaviour of conductivity at various temperatures.[106]

As far as the solid state conductivity is concerned, the data published so far are insufficient to elucidate the behaviour of the complexes. An interesting observation is that the specific conductivity increases suddenly on fusion in the case of several complexes, e.g. ammonium fluoroborate,[109] boron trifluoride-dihydrate (N. N. Greenwood and R. L. Martin, ref. 101, p. 1915) and boron trifluoride–(mono) acetic acid (loc. cit., p. 1795).

An important case of solid complexes is that of quinone and chloranil species.[122] Most of the quinone molecular complexes with electrical resistivities of $10^6$ ohm cm or less have essentially dative ground states. However, this does not apply to the $p$-chloranil or $p$-bromanil–1,6-diaminopyrene complexes, which have resistivities of about $10^3$ ohm cm. Similar considerations apply to the complexes formed by $p$-benzoquinone derivatives, such as dichlorodibromo or trichloromonobromo compounds, with the diaminopyrene. In the case of the chloranil complex the preparation via a chloroform solution gives dark blue crystals; the resistivity of the pelleted sample is about $10^7$ ohm cm. But if the complex is crystallized out from a benzene solution, a brown solid is obtained with a resistivity of about $10^5$ ohm cm; a compressed sample of the brown variety has a resistivity of only a few ohm centimetres. Both the green and brown complexes seem to have non-bonding ground states, as confirmed by absorption and diffuse reflectance spectra. The existence of these polymorphic forms has been confirmed by X-ray diffraction and spectroscopic studies.

The problem of solutions of boron trifluoride complexes is rather difficult in view of the possibility of interaction with the solvent;[110] an important case[111] is that of sulphur dioxide solutions, since this solvent is a potential addend which is known to form a complex $BF_3SO_2$ at $-96°C$. Despite these difficulties a large number of solutions have been examined. Thus the alkali fluoroborates are strong electrolytes in aqueous solution, while the ammonium complex behaves like an electrolyte in ethanol.[109]

Some of the diacoholates in nitrobenzene solution conduct electricity[112] while solutions of $BF_3NH_3$ in liquid ammonia received a great deal of attention on that account.[113]

(v) *Transition points.* Very little information can be gained from the study of melting or boiling points of boron trifluoride complexes. There is no single relation between the melting point and the composition of the complex or with the chain length of the donor molecule (ref. 98, p. 19). Most molecular complexes of boron trifluoride either thermally dissociate or decompose in the vapour phase, so that the "boiling point" is not used as a reliable guide to characterising complexes[114] (see also ref. 101, p. 751).

(vi) *Density and molar volumes.* The density of most of the boron trifluoride complexes may be expressed by the relation[115]

$$d_4^{20} \text{ (complex)} = \frac{M \text{ (complex)}}{V_M \text{ (donor)} + 28},$$

where $M$ is the molecular weight and $V_M$ is the molar volume. The figure 28 represents the molar volume of co-ordinated boron trifluoride acceptor ($28 \text{ cm}^3$), since

$$\Delta V_M = V_M \text{ (complex)} - V_M \text{ (donor)} = 28.$$

This figure is less than that giving the molar volume of free boron trifluoride either as a liquid ($\approx 39$) or as a solid ($\approx 35$). For the solid complexes,[115] the mean value of $\Delta V_M$ is 25 while that for $BF_3 \cdot 2H_2O$ is abnormally low (14·9) because of the fact that water expands rather than contracts on freezing.

(vii) *Vapour pressure and Trouton's coefficient.* In general the vapour pressures of the molecular complexes are considerably less than those of the parent donors. The values obtained must, however, be treated with some caution since thermal dissociation is liable to occur in the vapour phase.[116] This vapour-phase dissociation is also reflected in the values for the Trouton co-efficient, which is about 21 for normal liquids; higher values point to dissociation in the vapour phase or association in the liquid phase. For many boron trifluoride complexes[117] the Trouton coefficient is greater than 21, e.g. it is 26·8 for $BF_3 \cdot Me_3N$ and

30·3 for $BF_3 \cdot Me_2O$ (see also A. W. Laubengayer and G. R. Finlay, ref. 102).

(viii) *Geometry of molecular complexes.* The earliest tentative theoretical predictions on the geometry of molecular complexes were based[2] on two assumptions: (a) that only one dative function of lowest energy is important from a configurational point of view, and (b) that arbitrary assignments of values to various terms in the equations relating the energy of the charge-transfer band to the ionization potential of the donor are plausible. The first assumption is in many cases too simple, though for amine–halogen complexes, e.g. $C_6H_5N–XY$ or $R_3N–XY$, where $XY$ is ICl or $I_2$, the axially symmetric model is in agreement with the predictions based on assumption (a);[30] the atoms $N–X–Y$ lie on a straight line, which coincides with the symmetry axis of the donor moiety, so that maximum overlap arises between the lone-pair donor and acceptor molecular orbitals. It is also postulated that the complex in solution has the same geometry as the solid.[41] It must be noted, however, that Hassel's model for amine–halogen complexes was not anticipated on the basis of certain assumptions about the magnitude of various terms in the charge-transfer energy equations, as postulated in assumption (b).[118]

The geometry of solid complexes formed by $n$-donors with halogens has been investigated by Hassel and co-workers.[30, 119] X-ray diffraction studies of the crystals of complexes formed by dioxane, dithiane or $S_8$ as $n$-donors, with organic halides, such as iodoform or oxalyl bromide, showed that the distances between the halogen atoms and the $n$-donor atoms are markedly shorter than the van der Waals distances and that the complexes are charge-transfer species, though there is some doubt about the importance of the charge-transfer forces in these adducts. Another structure investigated is the pyridine–iodine ($Py \cdot 2I_2$) complex; this was found to be composed of $[Py–I–Py]^+$ and $I_3^-$ and $I_2$ units associated in the same way as in the $I_7^-$ ion, the N–I distance being slightly shorter than that found in molecular complexes. Similarly, Hassel found that the picoline–iodine complex was a true molecular complex. This work has been fully reviewed by Briegleb.[40]

The solid state geometry of the strong complexes between

*n*-donors and halogens, as studied by X-ray diffraction, displays a common characteristic in that the distance between the donor atom and the first halogen atom is significantly shorter than the van der Waals distance, while that between the halogen atoms is longer than in the free halogen molecule. Similar considerations apply to the solid complexes formed by iodine with the sulphur and selenium analogues of dioxane.[120]

As regards the geometrical structure of complexes of $\pi$-donors and halogens, the problem is far from having been solved.[41] For instance, various views are advanced concerning the structure of complexes of benzene and chlorine or bromine. Solid state studies indicate that the complex is a closed-packed crystal composed of postively charged discs and negatively charged rods in a 1:1 ratio, i.e. the halogen molecule is perpendicular to the benzene ring, lies on a sixfold axis of symmetry, and is equidistant between two benzene rings, while chains of alternating benzene and halogen molecules run through the crystal. This "axial" model cannot, however, be true for solutions, since in the solid each halogen molecule interacts with two or more benzene molecules, while in solution it does so with only one aromatic molecule. Similarly, other models proposed, e.g. "resting model" (halogen axis parallel to the benzene plane) or "oblique model"[2] are not based on convincing evidence. The quantum-mechanical aspect of the benzene complexes is discussed in Chapter 2 of this book (pp. 15–19), while the geometry of other complexes studied by means of X-ray diffraction is reviewed in Chapter 3 (pp. 69–73). As far as the structures of weak $\pi$-complexes are concerned, there is agreement between theoretical prediction and experimental evidence. Thus for solid $\pi$-complexes the principle of maximum overlap leads to structures in which the donor and acceptor planes lie parallel in the crystal at approximately van der Waals distance apart.[121]

## References

1. M. L. JOSIEN and J. LASCOMBE, *Coll. Intern. Centre Natl. Recherche Sci. (Paris)*, 1959, **77**, 137.
2. R. S. MULLIKEN, *J. Amer. Chem. Soc.*, 1952, **74**, 811.

3. L. E. ORGEL and R. S. MULLIKEN, *J. Amer. Chem. Soc.*, 1957, **79**, 4839.
4. S. F. MASON, *Quart. Revs. (London)*, 1961, **15**, 353.
5. G. BRIEGLEB and J. CZEKALLA, *Angew. Chem.*, 1960, **72**, 401.
6. E. M. KOSOWER, *J. Amer. Chem. Soc.*, 1958, **80**, 3253, 3261, 3267.
7. M. SMITH and M. C. R. SYMONS, *Trans. Faraday Soc.*, 1958, **54**, 338, 346.
8. E. M. KOSOWER *et al.*, *J. Chem. Phys.*, 1957, **26**, 1353; G. STEIN and A. TREININ, *Trans. Faraday Soc.*, 1959, **55**, 1086, 1091; J. JORTNER *et al.*, ibid., 1960, **56**, 1274; T. R. GRIFFITHS and M. C. R. SYMONS, ibid., 1960, **56**, 1125.
9. K. NAKAMOTO, *J. Amer. Chem. Soc.*, 1952, **74**, 1739.
10. R. S. MULLIKEN, *J. Phys. Chem.*, 1952, **56**, 801.
11. S. P. MCGLYNN, Ph. D. Dissertation, Florida State Univ., 1956.
12. G. BRIEGLEB and J. CZEKALLA, *Z. Elektrochem.*, 1955, **59**, 184.
13. W. C. PRICE, *Chem. Revs.*, 1957, **57**, 257; C. E. CASTRO *et al.*, *J. Amer. Chem. Soc.*, 1958, **80**, 2322; R. FOSTER and D. LL. HAMMICK, *J. Chem. Soc.*, 1954, 2685; H. MURAKAMI, *Bull. Chem. Soc. Japan*, 1954, **27**, 1268.
14. H. MURAKAMI, *Bull. Chem. Soc. Japan*, 1955, **28**, 577, 581.
15. G. BRIEGLEB and J. CZEKALLA, *Z. phys. Chem.*, 1960, **24**, 37.
16. R. S. MULLIKEN, *Rec. Trav. Chim.*, 1956, **75**, 845.
17. N. OGINACHI *et al.*, *J. Amer. Chem. Soc.*, 1955, **77**, 4202.
18. D. F. EVANS, *J. Chem. Phys.*, 1955, **23**, 1424, 1426; id., *J. Chem. Soc.*, 1957, 4229; H. MURAKAMI, *J. Chem. Phys.*, 1955, **23**, 1957.
19. S. H. HASTINGS *et al.*, *J. Amer. Chem. Soc.*, 1953, **75**, 2900.
20. A. U. MUNCK and J. F. SCOTT, *Nature (London)*, 1956, **177**, 587.
21. D. F. EVANS, *J. Chem. Soc.*, 1957, 4229; G. KÖRTUM, *Z. phys. Chem.*, 1939, **B43**, 271.
22. W. B. JEPSON and J. S. ROWLINSON, *J. Chem. Soc.*, 1956, 1278; G. KÖRTUM and W. M. VOGEL, *Z. Elektrochem.*, 1955, **59**, 16.
23. J. N. MURRELL, *J. Amer. Chem. Soc.*, 1958, **81**, 5037.
24. L. J. ANDREWS and R. M. KEEFER, *J. Amer. Chem. Soc.*, 1952, **74**, 4500.
25. N. J. SMITH, Ph. D. Thesis, Univ. of Chicago, Ill., 1955.
26. J. BURGERS *et al.*, *Rec. Trav. Chim.*, 1958, **77**, 491.
27. J. A. A. KETELAAR, *J. Phys. Radium*, 1954, **15**, 197.
28. D. R. STEPHENS and H. G. DRICKAMER, *J. Chem. Phys.*, 1959, **30**, 1518.
29. J. N. MURRELL, *J. Amer. Chem. Soc.*, 1959, **81**, 5037.
30. O. HASSEL, *Mol. Phys.*, 1958, **1**, 241.
31. D. BOOTH *et al.*, *Trans. Faraday Soc.*, 1959, **55**, 1293.
32. J. CZEKALLA, *Z. Elektrochem.*, 1959, **63**, 1157.
33. J. N. MURRELL, *Quart. Revs. (London)*, 1961, **15**, 191.
34. S. P. MCGLYNN and J. D. BOGGUS, *J. Amer. Chem. Soc.*, 1958, **80**, 5096.
35. A. BIER, *Rec. Trav. Chim.*, 1956, **75**, 866.
36. J. MCCONNELL *et al.*, *J. Chem. Phys.*, 1953, **21**, 66.
37. R. FOSTER, *Tetrahedron*, 1960, **10**, 96.
38. S. NAGAKURA, *J. Amer. Chem. Soc.*, 1958, **80**, 520; J. COLLIN, *Bull. Soc. Roy. Sci., Liège*, 1954, **23**, 395.
39. E. M. KOSOWER, *J. Amer. Chem. Soc.*, 1956, **78**, 5700.
40. G. BRIEGLEB, *Elektronen-Donator-Acceptor-Komplexe*, Springer-Verlag, Berlin, 1961.
41. R. S. MULLIKEN, *Ann. Rev. Phys. Chem.*, 1962, **13**, 107.
42. J. COLLINS, *Z. Elektrochem.*, 1960, **64**, 936.
43. H. YADA *et al.*, *Bull. Chem. Soc. Japan*, 1960, **33**, 1660.

44. S. D. Ross et al., J. Amer. Chem. Soc., 1956, **78**, 3625.
45. S. P. McGlynn, Chem. Revs., 1958, **58**, 1113.
46. S. K. Chakrabarty and A. K. Chandra, Naturw., 1962, **49**, 206.
47. S. F. Mason, J. Chem. Soc., 1960, 2437.
48. R. E. Merrifield and W. D. Phillips, J. Amer. Chem. Soc., 1958, **80**, 2778.
49. H. M. Powell et al., J. Chem. Soc., 1943, 153.
50. R. Beukers and A. Szent-Györgyi, Rec. Trav. Chim., 1962, **81**, 255.
51. W. L. Peticolas, J. Chem. Phys., 1957, **26**, 429.
52. G. Dallinga, Acta Cryst., 1954, **7**, 665.
53. E. E. Ferguson and F. A. Matsen, J. Chem. Phys., 1958, **29**, 105.
54. G. Briegleb and J. Czekalla, Z. Elektrochem., 1959, **63**, 6.
55. H. J. Taufen et al., J. Amer. Chem. Soc., 1941, **63**, 3500.
56. J. Collins and L. D'Or, J. Chem. Phys., 1955, **23**, 397.
57. L. D'Or et al., Rec. Trav. Chim., 1956, **75**, 862.
58. W. B. Person et al., J. Chem. Phys., 1957, **27**, 211; id., J. Amer. Chem. Soc., 1958, **80**, 2940.
59. E. E. Ferguson, J. Chem. Phys., 1956, **25**, 577; id. ibid., 1957, **26**, 1265.
60. G. C. Pimental et al., J. Chem. Phys., 1951, **19**, 513.
61. A. N. Terenin, Uspekhi Khim., 1955, **24**, 121.
62. A. N. Terenin, Izvest. Akad. Nauk SSSR, Ser. Fiz., 1958, **22**, 1100.
63. V. N. Filimonov et al., Optika i Spektroskopiya, 1957, **3**, 480.
64. P. Chalandon and B. P. Susz, Helv. Chim. Acta, 1958, **41**, 697.
65. H. Luther et al., J. Prakt. Chem., 1958, **5**, 242.
66. E. K. Plyler and R. S. Mulliken, J. Amer. Chem. Soc., 1959, **81**, 823.
67. A. I. Popov et al., J. Amer. Chem. Soc., 1961, **83**, 3586.
68. I. Y. Chang and E. E. Ferguson, J. Chem. Phys., 1961, **34**, 628.
69. W. B. Person et al., J. Chem. Phys., 1961, **35**, 908.
70. E. E. Ferguson and F. A. Matsen, J. Amer. Chem. Soc., 1960, **82**, 3268.
71. W. B. Person et al., J. Amer. Chem. Soc., 1960, **82**, 29; R. A. Zingaro and W. E. Tolberg, ibid., 1959, **81**, 1353; W. D. Jones and W. T. Simpson, J. Chem. Phys., 1960, **32**, 1747; H. B. Friedrich, Ph. D. Thesis, Iowa, 1962.
72. W. B. Person et al., J. Amer. Chem. Soc., 1959, **81**, 273.
73. D. L. Glusker and H. W. Thompson, J. Chem. Soc., 1955, 471.
74. C. Reid, J. Chem. Phys., 1952, **20**, 1212; M. M. Moodie and C. Reid, ibid., 1954, **22**, 252.
75. E. Clar and M. Zander, Chem. Ber., 1956, **89**, 799.
76. J. Czekalla et al., Z. Elektrochem., 1957, **61**, 537.
77. S. P. McGlynn et al., J. Chem. Phys., 1960, **32**, 357.
78. Ng. Ph. Buu-Hoï and P. Jacquignon, Bull. Soc. Chim. France, 1957, 488.
79. M. Kasha, Disc. Faraday Soc., 1950, **9**, 14.
80. R. F. Vassil'ev, Nature (London), 1962, **196**, 668; id. ibid., 1963, **300**, 773; R. F. Vassil'ev et al., Dokl. Akad. Nauk SSSR, 1963, **149**, 124.
81. S. S. Bhatnagar and C. L. Lakra, Indian J. Phys., 1933, **8**, 43; N. S. Rao and S. R. Gavindarayan, Proc. Indian Acad. Sci., 1942, **15A**, 33.
82. R. Sahney et al., J. Indian Chem. Soc., 1946, **23**, 335.
83. H. Kainer et al., Naturw., 1954, **41**, 303.
84. B. Bleaney and K. W. H. Stevens, Rept. Progr. Phys., 1953, **16**, 108.
85. H. Akamatsu et al., Bull. Chem. Soc. Japan, 1956, **29**, 213.
86. H. Akamatsu et al., Bull. Chem. Soc. Japan, 1957, **30**, 618.

87. Y. Matsunaga, *Bull. Chem. Soc. Japan*, 1955, **28**, 475.
88. H. M. Buck *et al.*, *Mol. Phys.*, 1958, **1**, 196.
89. G. Briegleb and J. Czekalla, *Naturw.*, 1954, **41**, 448; J. Czekalla, Z. *Elektrochem.*, 1956, **60**, 145; H. Tsubomura, *Bull. Chem. Soc. Japan*, 1954, **27**, 1.
90. G. Körtum and H. Walz, *Z. Elektrochem.*, 1953, **57**, 73.
91. R. S. Mulliken, *J. Chim. Phys.*, 1954, **51**, 341; id., *J. Amer. Chem. Soc.*, 1954, **76**, 3869.
92. P. Gagnaux *et al.*, *Helv. Chim. Acta*, 1958, **41**, 1023.
93. G. Körtum, *J. Chim. Phys.*, 1952, **49**, C. 129.
94. Ya. K. Syrkin and K. M. Anisimova, *Dokl. Akad. Nauk SSSR*, 1948, **59**, 1457.
95. W. Strohmeier and D. v. Hobe, *Z. Elektrochem.*, 1960, **64**, 445.
96. R. Linke and W. Rohrmann, *Z. phys. Chem.*, 1937, **B35**, 256.
97. J. A. Pople, *Proc. Roy. Soc.*, 1950, **A202**, 323.
98. N. N. Greenwood and R. L. Martin, *Quart. Revs. (London)*, 1954, **8**, 1.
99. H. E. Watson and K. L. Ramaswamy, *Proc. Roy. Soc.*, 1936, **A156**, 144.
100. W. Pannwitz, *J. Prakt. Chem.*, 1934, **141**, 123.
101. A. V. Topchiev and Ya. M. Paushkin, *Uspekh. Khim.*, 1947, **16**, 664; N. N. Greenwood and R. L. Martin, *J. Chem. Soc.*, 1951, 1795, 1915; id. ibid., 1953, 751, 757; N. N. Greenwood *et al.*, ibid., 1950, 3030.
102. S. Sugden and M. Waloff, *J. Chem. Soc*, 1932, 1492; E. Wiberg and W. Mathing, *Ber.*, 1937, **70**, 690; A. W. Laubengayer and G. R. Finlay, *J. Amer. Chem. Soc.*, 1943, **65**, 884.
103. A. W. Laubengayer *et al.*, *J. Amer. Chem. Soc.*, 1941, **63**, 559.
104. F. J. Sowa *et al.*, *J. Amer. Chem. Soc.*, 1933, **55**, 3402; A. V. Topchiev *et al.*, *Dokl. Akad. Nauk SSSR*, 1951, **80**, 381, 611.
105. A. A. Wolf and N. N. Greenwood, *J. Chem. Soc.*, 1950, 2200.
106. N. N. Greenwood and R. L. Martin, *J. Chem. Soc.*, 1953, 1427.
107. N. N. Greenwood *et al.*, *J. Chem. Soc.*, 1951, 1328.
108. R. L. Burwell and L. M. Elkin, *J. Amer. Chem. Soc.*, 1951, **73**, 502; id. ibid. 1952, **74**, 4567.
109. D. R. Martin and J. K. Riecke, *J. Amer. Chem. Soc.*, 1951, **73**, 5895.
110. L. A. O'Leary and H. H. Wenzke, *J. Amer. Chem. Soc.*, 1933, **55**, 2117.
111. H. S. Booth and D. R. Martin, *J. Amer. Chem. Soc.*, 1942, **64**, 2198.
112. H. Meerwein, *Ber.*, 1933, **66**, 411.
113. H. Schmenken, Ph. D. Dissertation, Göttingen, 1946; J. Goubeau, *F.I.A.T. Revs. of German Science; Inorganic Chemistry*, **1**, 217.
114. H. Bowlus and J. A. Nieuwland, *J. Amer. Chem. Soc.*, 1931, **53**, 3855; G. T. Morgan and R. Taylor, *J. Chem. Soc.*, 1932, 1497; H. Meerwein and W. Pannwitz, *J. Prakt. Chem.*, 1934, **141**, 123; H. Meerwein and D. Vossen, ibid., 1934, **141**, 149.
115. N. N. Greenwood and R. L. Martin, *J. Chem. Soc.*, 1953, 4132.
116. J. H. de Boer and J. A. M. van Liempt, *Rec. Trav. Chim.*, 1927, **46**, 124; E. Pohland and W. Harlos, *Z. anorg. Chem.*, 1932, **207**, 242; L. J. Klinkenberg, *Rec. Trav. Chim.*, 1937, **56**, 36; H. C. Brown *et al.*, *J. Amer. Chem. Soc.*, 1939, **61**, 673; A. W. Laubengayer and D. S. Sears, ibid., 1945, **67**, 164.
117. A. B. Burg and A. A. Green, *J. Amer. Chem. Soc.*, 1943, **65**, 1838.
118. G. Reid and R. S. Mulliken, *J. Chem. Phys.*, 1954, **76**, 3869.

119. O. HASSEL and K. O. STRØMME, *Nature (London)*, 1958, **182**, 1155; T. BJORVATTEN and O. HASSEL, *Acta Chem. Scand.*, 1959, **13**, 1261; O. HASSEL, *Svensk Kem. Tidskr.*, 1960, **72**:2, 88; id., *Tiddskr. Kjemi Bergvesen Met.*, 1961, **3**, 60; id., *Nature (London)*, 1961, **189**, 137; P. GROTH and O. HASSEL, *Proc. Chem. Soc.*, Sept., 1961, 343; O. HASSEL and H. HOPE, *Acta Chem. Scand.*, 1961, **15**, 407; O. HASSEL *et al.*, ibid., 1961, **15**, 967.

120. J. D. McCULLOUGH *et al.*, *Acta Cryst.*, 1959, **12**, 815; G. Y. CHAO and J. D. McCULLOUGH, ibid., 1960, **13**, 727; id. ibid., 1961, **14**, 940.

121. S. C. WALLWORK, *J. Chem. Soc.*, 1961, 494.

122. Y. MATSUNAGA, *Nature (London)*, 1965, **205**, 72; id. ibid., 1966, **211**, 183.

123. K. M. C. DAVIS and M. C. R. SYMONS, *J. Chem. Soc.*, 1965, 2079.

# CHAPTER 5

# EFFECT OF STRUCTURES OF DONORS AND ACCEPTORS ON COMPLEX FORMATION

IN GENERAL the introduction of substituents, which increase the electron density of the ring, enhances the stability of the complex, as shown by the relative values of the stability constants. For example, the stability constants of the 1 : 1 molecular complexes formed in aqueous solutions by monosubstituted benzene (*D*) and the silver ion, viz.

$$D + Ag^+ \rightleftharpoons Ag. D^+$$

increase in the order of substituents $NO_2 < F < COMe < COEt < Cl < Br < OH < H < OMe$; this is also the order in which the substituents enhance the electron density of the aromatic ring, as determined by their effect on the rates and positions of electrophilic aromatic substitution.[1] The case of iodine is exceptional in that this halogen increases the value of the stability constant to a considerable extent. This abnormal enhancement has been attributed to the preferential co-ordination of the silver ion to the iodine atom instead of the aromatic nucleus.[2] The even higher value for styrene (id. ibid., 1950, **72**, 5034) is probably due to the co-ordination of the silver ion at the vinyl side-chain. These effects are magnified still further in the case of the tetranitromethane acceptor.[3]

The number of substituents in the donor molecule also plays an important part in determining the stabilities of addition complexes. Thus the stability constants of complexes involving polymethyl benzenes as donors and all acceptor types, except the silver ions, increase with the number of methyl groups in the aromatic molecule.[3,4,5,6,7] This enhancement is due to the fact that the methyl substituents increase the electron density of the aromatic nucleus through induction and hyperconjugation. It should be observed, however, that this general increase of the relative stabilities of the complexes with the increasing number of methyl substituents varies widely for different acceptors. The changes are small with acceptors, such as iodine, hydrogen chloride or iodine chloride; indeed, the enhancement in the case of hydrogen chloride is negligible and it is probably due to experimental errors.[6] On the other hand, large changes occur in the case of acceptors, such as hydrogen fluoride or hydrogen fluoride–boron trifluoride.[6,7,8] For instance, the stability constants of the hydrogen fluoride complexes of methyl-, $p$-dimethyl-, 1,2,4,-trimethyl-, 1,2,4,5-tetramethyl-, pentamethyl- and hexamethyl-benzenes are in the ratio 0·63 : 1 : 63 : 140 : 29,000 : 97,000. The comparable ratios for the HF–BF$_3$ acceptor system are 0·01 : 1 : 40 : 120 : 8700 : 89,000. Furthermore, an increase in the number of rings in the donor molecules, leads, in the absence of unfavourable steric effects, to an increase in the values of stability constants of 1 : 1 complexes, e.g. iodine,[5] tetranitromethane[3] or maleic anhydride[9] 1 : 1 complexes of naphthalene are more stable than those of benzene. In some cases, however, this phenomenon is mainly due to steric considerations.[10]

An interesting group of molecular complexes involving 1,3,5-trinitrobenzene was investigated by Tronov *et al.*[10] The other moiety was aniline, $m$- and $o$-toluidine and 3,4-xylidine. He found that the amines have greater ability to form complexes if they contain more methyl groups in the ring, since these groups raise the electron density of the benzene ring. Similar considerations apply to complexes formed by 3,4-xylidine with 2,4,6-trinitrotoluene or trinitromesitylene. However, complex formation in the case of nitro-aromatics is influenced not only by the electronic character of the methyl substituents, but also by their steric effects. If the latter disrupt coplanarity and conjugation, then the ability to form complexes is more reduced than in the case when the steric effect simply screens off functional groups.

There are, however, a number of exceptions to the rule concerning the effect of electron densities of the aromatic moiety on stability constants of molecular complexes. For instance, the addition products of nitro-substituted benzenes are more stable than those of benzene itself,[11] though nitro-groups are strongly electron-attracting. This anomaly appears to be due to specific interactions between the acceptors and the nitro-groups of the donor.[12] Similarly in the case of α-substituted naphthalenes reacting with s-trinitrobenzene the ethoxy and hydrogen groups are out of place in the series of substituents that increase the electron density in the aromatic nucleus. Another exception is provided by the complexes formed between substituted anilines and 2,4-dinitrochlorobenzene in ethanol solution.[13,14] Ross and Kuntz[14] give, in addition, full thermodynamic data for the molecular complexes formed between anthracene and a series of 1-substituted 2,4,6-trinitrobenzene in chloroform solution, or between 1,3,5,-trinitrobenzene and substituted anilines in ethanol solution. It is possible, however, that this anomaly is due to solvation effects in polar solvents, similarly to the cases of silver-ion complexes of polyalkylbenzenes in aqueous solutions; thus the durene and mesitylene complexes are of low stability, since the water molecules in the hydration sphere of the silver ion hinder the approach of the metallic ion to the aromatic nucleus because of the overlap of methyl groups.[1]

It is evident that, in general, favourable electronic influences are opposed by unfavourable steric effects, e.g. in the interaction between aromatic hydrocarbons and methanol[15] or chloroform,[16] and picric acid and benzanthracene.[10] In the last case, the twelve monomethyl-1,2-benzanthracene picrates have higher melting points than the acid itself with the exception of the 1-methyl and 9-methyl-1,2-benzanthracenes. This is explained by noting that in the 9-methyl compound the 9-methyl group overlaps the 1-hydrogen so that the acid cannot easily approach the hydrocarbon plane; hence the low stability and low melting point. Another example of the influence of steric hindrance is the lack of complex formation between rubrene and m-dinitrobenzene,[17] because of the position of the four phenyl groups in the hydrocarbon molecule.

The isomer effect must also be considered in connection with structural studies of the components of molecular complexes. Investigations of interactions between the acceptors m-dinitrobenzene or p-benzoquinone with the donors m- or p-dihydroxybenzene, or $m$- or $p$-diaminobenzene, indicate that in alcoholic solutions at various temperatures the $m$-donor–$m$-acceptor complex is more stable than the $p$-donor–$m$-acceptor product,[18] while the $p$-donor–$p$-acceptor complex is more stable than that formed between the $m$-donor and $p$-acceptor.

Finally, one must note that the electronegativity of atoms in donor molecules is also of importance. For instance,[19] in the case of the boron trifluoride acceptor the sequence of donating power of $Me_2O$, $Me_2S$ and $Me_2Se$ is in the order $O > S > Se$; for borine and trimethylboron, however, it is in the order $S > Se$, $O$; the borine adduct is more stable than the $BF_3$ analogue, so that $B_2H_6$ displaces $BF_3$ from $Me_3P–BF_3$, while the usual order of the trifluoride towards Group IIIB acceptors is $P > N > As >$ Sb, towards $BH_3$ it is $N > P > As > Sb$. As regards $Me_2S$ and $Me_2Se$, the order of stability is $BH_3 > BF_3 > BMe_3$ at $-22°C$. Hence the following reactions take place

$$2Me_2S \cdot BF_3 + B_2H_6 \rightarrow 2Me_2S \cdot BH_3 + 2BF_3$$

Also $B_2H_6$ displaces quantitatively $BF_3$ from $Me_3P \cdot BF_3$ at $80°C$ in 22 hr ($Me_3N$ displaces $Me_3P$ completely under the same conditions). The ability of an atom to donate a lone pair is often reduced by the presence of electron-attracting groups in the donor moiety. For instance, the complexes $BF_3–PF_3$ and $BF_3–PCl_3$ do not exist, while $BF_3–PH_3$ is known.[20] On the other hand, considerations other than electronegativity are also of importance. Thus,[21] $BF_3–AsH_3$ does not form even below $-100°C$, whereas $BCl_3–AsH_3$ and $BBr_3–AsH_3$ are known;[22] similarly, $BCl_3–CNMe$ is more stable than the fluoride complex.[23] Clearly, other factors are of importance, and a fuller discussion is given in Chapter 6.

### The effect of acceptor structure

A useful classification of acceptors into ten types has been given by Andrews (Ref. 13, pp. 732–50). These are (in alphabetical order):

1. Acid anhydrides, nitriles and acid chlorides.
2. Alcohols and water.

3. Halogens and certain halogen compounds.
4. Halomethanes.
5. Halogen halides, including $HF-BF_3$, $HCl-AlCl_3$ or similar species, and various acids, such as sulphuric, acetic and perchloric acids.
6. Metallic ions and salts.
7. Nitro-compounds, including the ubiquitous picric acid.
8. Quinones and their derivatives.
9. Sulphur compounds, e.g. oxides or chlorides.
10. Triphenylmethane and its derivatives.

By far the largest group of donor–acceptor complexes is made up of the Group 7 compounds.

The main features of the interactions between the compounds of the ten acceptor groups and various donors are shown in Table 5.1.

Recently a series of new acceptors have been investigated, e.g. cyanocarbons,[33] iodoform and oxalyl bromide,[34] pyromellitic dianhydride,[35] tetrachlorophthalic anhydride,[36] heteroaromatic compounds,[37] tropyllium ion[38] and iodine atom.[39] Of the above acceptors, tetrachlorophthalic anhydride, tetracyanoethylene, tropyllium ion and pyromellitic dianhydride are $\pi$-acceptors, the last being one of the strongest $\pi$-acceptors known.[40] On the other hand, carbonyl cyanide is intermediate between the strongest and strong acceptors, when reacting in $n$-hexane with a variety of donors, e.g. methylbenzene, polycyclic aromatic hydrocarbons, etc.[79]

The effect of the nature of the acceptor species on the stability of the molecular complex follows broadly that of the donor molecule. The nature and positions of the substituents in the acceptor molecule also affects the stability of the interaction products to a marked extent. In general the stability of the complexes is enhanced by increasing substitution by nitro or other electron-withdrawing groups in the acceptor ring. For instance, the 1,5-dinitronaphthalene complex with aniline is much more stable than that of $\alpha$-nitronaphthalene with the same aromatic base.[11] In the case of nitro derivatives of benzene, the stability constant of the $1:1$ $s$-trinitrobenzene–aniline complex in chloroform solution is about seven times as large as the interaction product between $m$- or $p$- dinitrobenzene with the base.[41]

Furthermore, $s$-trinitrobenzene forms many more complexes than does picric acid;[42] this is explained by considering the electron-donating properties of the methyl groups relative to that of hydrogen. In general, for polynitro-aromatic acceptors the stabilities of the corresponding complexes may be arranged in an order which reflects the electron-withdrawing power of the substituent group[43] in the acceptor molecule, viz., $COCl >$ $COOCH_3 > CONH_2$; $SO_2Cl > SO_2CH_3 > SOCH_3$; $NO_2 >$ $CN > COOCH_3$. On the other hand, steric effects are also important. Thus substitution on a carbon adjacent to a nitro-group opposes the effect of the nitro substituent. For example,[44] the stabilities of the dinitrotoluene complexes are in decreasing order, 2,4 or 2,5 or 3,5 > 2,6 > 2,3 or 3,4; those of the trinitrobenzenes are 1,3,5 > 1,2,3 or 1,2,4. In these cases ortho-substitution prevents the nitro-group from being in the plane of the acceptor ring. The above findings are in agreement with the experimental observations concerning the complexes formed by anthracene with 1-substituted-2,4,6-trinitrobenzenes in chloroform solutions (ref. 13, p. 752). Similar considerations apply to donor species as discussed previously.[45]

The case of the boron halides acting as acceptors is worthy of attention. Trimethylamine–boron trifluoride is the most stable member of the series involving the acceptors[46] (in order of decreasing stability) $BF_3 > BF_2Me > BFMe_2 > BMe_3$. The stability of the molecular complexes incorporating the above donors decreases with the gradual removal of the fluorine component, since the latter element is highly electronegative, while the alkyl groups are electron-releasing; in agreement with this, the nitrogen–boron dative bond in the $Me_3N–BF_3$ complex is highly polar owing to the considerable electron transfer to the acceptor atom. The dative-bond strength is, of course, also affected by the groups present in the donor moiety (cf. p. 123). It is important, however, to note that the stability of a molecular complex is not always based on the above electronegativity considerations, even when the donor and acceptor atoms are those situated in the first row of the Periodic Table of elements. Indeed, it has been shown that, using nitrobenzene or pyridine donors,[47] the order of stability of complexes containing boron halide moieties is $BF_3 < BCl_3 < BBr_3$, and not the reverse, as

## TABLE 5.1. *Donor-acceptor interaction*

| Acceptor group | Donors (D) | Example donor-acceptor (D)–(A) | Donor-acceptor ratio | Structure | Ref. |
|---|---|---|---|---|---|
| 1 (Acid anhydrides, nitriles, acid chlorides) | Aromatic hydrocarbons and their derivatives; aromatic amines | Benzene–maleic anhydride | 1:1 | Similar to intermediates in Diels-Alder reactions | 9, 24 |
| 2 (Alcohols and water) | Aromatic hydrocarbons and their alkyl derivatives | Benzene–ethanol | Probably 1:3 | Probably hydrogen bonding | 25 |
| 3 (Halogens and some halogen compounds) | Aromatic hydrocarbons and their alkyl derivatives; aryl-ethylenes; halo-substituted aromatic hydrocarbons | m-xylene–chlorine | 1:1 | Probably $D^+Cl^+Cl^-$ canonical form; steric orientations of $D$ and $A$ uncertain | 26 |
| 4 (Halomethanes) | Aromatic hydrocarbons and their halo-derivatives | Benzene–carbon tetrabromide | 1:1 | Hydrogen bonding between $D$ and $A$; structure uncertain | 27 27a |
| 5 (Halogen halides, including $HF-BF_3$, $HCl-AlCl_3$, etc. and acids, e.g. $H_2SO_4$, $CH_3CO_2H$, $HClO_4$) | Aromatic hydrocarbons and their polyalkyls; halo- and nitro-derivatives of aromatic hydrocarbons; arylethylenes | Polymethylbenzene–hydrogen chloride | 1:1 | As above | 6, 25 |

| Acceptor group | Donors ($D$) | Example donor–acceptor ($D$)–($A$) | Donor–acceptor ratio | Structure | Ref. |
|---|---|---|---|---|---|
| 6 (Metallic ions and salts) | Aromatic hydrocarbons and their alkyl derivatives; phenols; aromatic amines | Benzene–silver perchlorate | 1:1 | Silver ion located away from the symmetry axis above and between the two carbons of the aromatic ring | 28 |
| 7 (Nitro-compounds, including picric acid) | Aromatic hydrocarbons and their alkyl and nitro-derivatives; aromatic amines; unsaturated aromatic ketones; phenols | Benzene–s-trinitro-benzene | 2:1 | Probably complex formation due to favourable polarization on $A$ owing to the approach of electron-rich $D$ | 29, 80 |
| 8 (Quinones and their derivatives) | Hydroquinone and its derivatives; phenols; aromatic hydrocarbons and their alkyl derivatives | Hydroquinone–benzoquinone | 1:1 | Resemble type 1, though some hydrogen bonding | 30 |
| 9 (Sulphur compounds e.g. oxides and chlorides) | Aromatic hydrocarbons and their alkyl and chloro-derivatives | Benzene–sulphur dioxide | 1:1 | Mostly $C_6H_6 \overset{+}{:} \, S \overset{O^-}{\underset{O}{\diagdown}}$  Similar to Group 3 | 31 |
| 10 (Triphenyl methane and derivatives) | Benzene and its substitution products; aromatic amines; thiophene | Benzene–triphenyl methane | 1:1 | Probable hydrogen bonding | 32 |

127

expected from electronegativity effects. Other factors, such as mesomerism, $\pi$-bonding, steric hindrance, etc., must also be considered (a fuller discussion of this topic is given in the next chapter).

## Uncharged $\pi$-electron acceptors

An important class of acceptor compounds is that having the general formula $C_wN_xO_yF_z$, as described by Hammond.[48] These substances are uncharged $\pi$-electron compounds, which have high electron affinities and are, in effect, organic Lewis acids. It is known that such compounds are good electron acceptors[49] and can be reduced by polarographic,[50] chemical[51] and photolytic[52] techniques to radicals that can be studied by electron-spin resonance. Moreover, these acceptors present a challenge to methods for measuring electron affinity[53] and exhibit interesting chemistry.[54] Hammond investigated these topics in some detail and confirmed various predictions concerning the properties of these organic Lewis acids.[48]

The properties of these substances are ascribed to the fact that in this class of $\pi$-electron systems one deals with high electron affinity, and, frequently, with high ionization potentials, as may be seen, for instance, from the polarographic reduction potentials of nitrobenzenes,[55] charge-transfer absorption of complexes of aniline, anisoles and other compounds,[56] and polarographic and magnetron studies of benzoquinones.[48,57] Electron impact ionization potentials of benzenes and pyridines also show this effect.[58]

It is reasonable to assume from the above brief review of the acceptors that compounds containing a high proportion of highly electronegative elements, e.g. nitrogen, oxygen or fluorine, will act as organic electrophiles and form stable molecular complexes with suitable donors. In effect the class $C_wN_xO_yF_z$ will satisfy these criteria. Hammond[48] cites in his paper 35 compounds; a few of these are shown in Fig. 5.1.

An interesting observation in this connection is that uncharged substituents containing highly electronegative elements have also large Hammett values.[59] These substituents are also, in general,

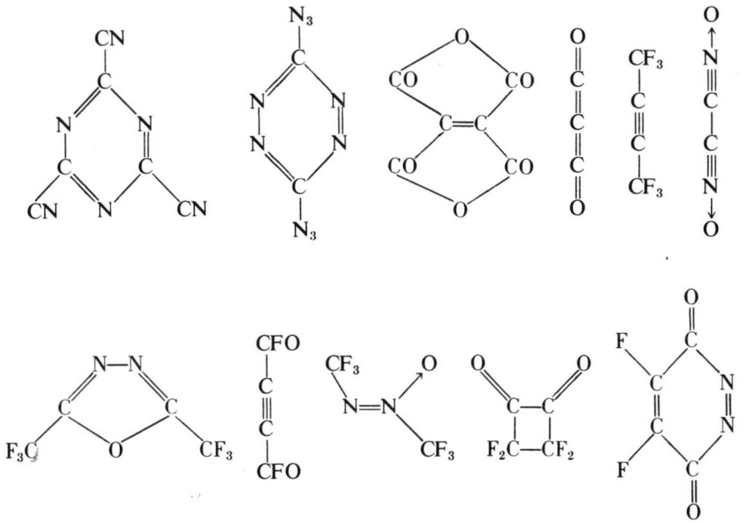

FIG. 5.1. Some examples of the organic electrophiles (acceptors).

highly unsaturated — in terms of the formula, this is equivalent to small values of $x$, $y$ and $z$ for any particular value of $w$; a high degree of unsaturation is required for a high electron affinity. Figure 5.1 shows some examples of carbon nitride, carbon oxide, carbon fluoride and multi-element compounds. In practice not all $\pi$-electron systems included in the formula are strong acceptors, nor are all organic acceptors restricted to the formula. On the other hand, the majority of the most powerful neutral, paired-electron acceptors are described by the formula $C_wN_xO_yF_w$. These compounds may still be acceptors, though they may contain other elements as well, provided there is a high degree of unsaturation in the substituents.

## Halogens as Lewis acids

Halogens may act as acceptors or Lewis acids,[13] forming loosely bonded interaction products with donors, such a numerous types of organic compounds that contain atoms with unshared electron pairs. These donors include aromatic compounds and those containing C—C multiple bonds. Here the electrons available for sharing are contained in $\pi$-molecular orbitals. Oxygen in many organic compounds can also act as a donor, e.g. in alcohols, ethers, carbonyl compounds, esters and acids; in the latter case, the weaker the acid, the more strongly it interacts with the halogen. For instance, acetic acid interacts more strongly with iodine to form a molecular complex than trifluoroacetic acid, which is very much stronger than the unsubstituted acid,[60] while the bond in the starch–iodine complexes may also result from the interaction between the halogen and oxygen of the carbohydrate.[61] As regards the other elements of Group VIB of the Periodic Table, the iodine adducts of 1:4-dithiane and 1:4-diselenane ($C_4H_8S_2 \cdot 2I_2$ and $C_4H_8Se_2 \cdot 2I_2$) are molecular complexes in which the iodine–iodine bond is unbroken,[62] (the strengths of the halogen–heteroatom bonds follow the order O < S < Se) while the products of interaction between the halogens and aromatic seleno-ethers are species in which both halogen atoms are covalently bonded to selenium.[63] Dibenzyl sulphide and alkyl halides also form 1:1 halogen complexes in solution[64] (see also ref. 62, O. Hassel); some solid complexes of iodine with aliphatic iodides have been precipitated at low temperatures,[65] while in solution they may serve as reaction intermediates.[66]

As seen above, 1:4-dithiane and 1:4-diselenane have two co-ordination sites. Similar considerations apply to nitrogen-containing compounds that act as donors. Thus 1:2-hexamethylenetetramine and bromine form a 1:2 donor–acceptor complex.[67] However, iodine or iodine monochloride forms a 1:1 complex with trimethylamine;[68] the same applies to pyridine[69] and other nitrogen-containing organic bases.[72]

The relative stabilities of complexes formed by a variety of donor molecules with halogen acceptors have been evaluated, particularly in the case of alkylbenzenes,[5] alkenes,[70] ethers[71] and nitrogen bases.[72] The first of these donors have been studied in detail[5] by spectrophotometric methods. Since it is reasonable to assume that complex stabilities and substitution rates of alkylbenzenes should both have a similar dependence on the availability of aromatic electrons, it follows that, in general, stabilities of molecular complexes incorporating alkylbenzenes should follow the same order as the ease of electrophilic substitution in the halogen donors[13] (p. 713). Thus the values of equilibrium constants of complexes formed by methylbenzenes with iodine monochloride increase with the number of methyl groups in the aromatic donor, from 0·87 l./mole for toluene to 22·7 l./mole for hexamethylbenzene. Furthermore, since halogen substitution in the methyl group of the alkyl aromatic compound deactivates the aromatic nucleus with respect to further substitution, therefore the complex formed by *m*-chlorotoluene with iodine monochloride will be less stable than that formed by toluene with the interhalogen compound.[73] One must note, however, that though the stabilities of these complexes appear to be, in general, but little influenced by the position of the alkyl groups in the alkyl aromatic compound, there are notable exceptions owing to steric considerations. For example, the stability of the complex formed by 1,3,5-tri-*tert*-butylbenzene with iodine monochloride is less than that expected for alkylbenzene donors; presumably, the bulk of the three side-chain groups inhibits their close approach to the $\pi$-electrons of the aromatic nucleus, so that the optimum stabilization conditions of the complex are not satisfied.[73] A similar situation arises in the case of the iodine acceptor (see ref. 71, Keefer and Andrews) and the butylbenzene donor.

Alkyl iodides display donor strengths similar to those of alkylbenzenes.[64] The stabilities of the complexes containing the alkyl iodide moiety depend on the ability of the alkyl groups to release electrons to the iodine atom of the donor molecule. On the other hand, the stabilities of the interaction products formed by iodine with alkenes fall between those of tri- and tetra-alkylbenzenes,[70, 74] but alkenes bearing a halogen atom at the carbon–carbon double bond have much lower donor strength. For instance,[74] the values of the stability constants $K_N$ (expressed in terms of mole fractions) of complexes of iodine with *cis*- and *trans*-dichloroethylenes are about 0·3, while that of di-isobutylene[70] with iodine in the same solvent (dioxane) and at the same temperature is 3·7; the relatively low donor strength of halo-alkenes may be due to unfavourable inductive effects of the chloro-substituents on $\pi$-electron availability. It is also interesting to note that cyclo-alkenes have comparable donor strengths to those of alkenes.[74, 75] In general the olefinic hydrocarbons are much stronger donors than cyclo-alkanes (ref. 39, Andrews and Keefer, p. 112).

As regards donor strengths of alcohols, ethers and alkyl-substituted ketones towards halogen acceptors, they are much greater than those of the alkenes and are similar to those of the highly alkylated benzenes[76] (also see ref. 71, Keefer and Andrews, p. 2164; DeMaine; Tideswell and McCullough; ref. 39 above).

An important feature concerning the donor properties of ethers is that the sulphur and selenium analogues of the ethers have greater donor strength with respect to iodine than the ethers themselves, since oxygen is more electronegative than the other elements of Group VIB (ref. 71, Tideswell and McCullough).

The strongest donors of all are nitrogen bases. For example, the stability constant of the 1:1 complex triethylamine–iodine in $n$-heptane at 25°C is over 200 times as large (ref. 72, S. Nagakura) as that of hexamethylbenzene, which, in turn, has the highest value for all methylbenzenes; those involving iodine monochloride or iodine monobromide acceptors are even higher. For instance, the $K_c$ values (in litres per mole) at 25°C in carbon tetrachloride solution of the complexes formed by the donor pyridine with iodine or iodine monochloride are 97 and $4 \cdot 9 \times 10^5$, respectively.[77] On the other hand, highly fluorinated aliphatic amines (ref. 72, E. Colton) or alcohols[78] are very poor donors because of the highly unfavourable inductive effect of the fluorine atom. Thus iodine gives a blue solution with the fluorinated amine $(C_4F_9)_3N$, i.e. no complex formation occurs – a behaviour similar to that shown by carbon tetrachloride or aliphatic hydrocarbons.

Finally, it is worth noting that there exist substances, which may act as acceptors and donors. For instance, the compound[81] 1,3-dimethylalloxazine acts as a donor towards tetracyanoethylene as acceptor, or as an acceptor towards pyrene as a donor. The complexes crystallize out from ethylene dichloride solutions in the ratio of two of the alloxazine to one of the other compound. Molecular orbital theory leads to the conclusion that alloxazine is a donor in the presence of a strong acceptor, and an acceptor in the presence of a strong donor.

## References

1. L. J. ANDREWS and R. M. KEEFER, *J. Amer. Chem. Soc.*, 1949, **71**, 3644.
2. L. J. ANDREWS and R. M. KEEFER, *J. Amer. Chem. Soc.*, 1950, **72**, 3133.
3. D. LL. HAMMICK and R. P. YOUNG, *J. Chem. Soc.*, 1936, 1463.
4. H. D. ANDERSON and D. LL. HAMMICK, *J. Chem. Soc.*, 1950, 1089.
5. L J. ANDREWS and R. M. KEEFER, *J. Amer. Chem. Soc.*, 1952, **74**, 4500.
6. H. C. BROWN and J. D. BRADY, *J. Amer. Chem. Soc.*, 1952, **74**, 3570.
7. M. KILPATRICK and F. E. LUBORSKY, *J. Amer. Chem. Soc.*, 1953, **75**, 577; A. KUBOYAMA, *Tokyo Kogyo, Shikensho Hoksku*, 1962, **57**, 546.
8. D. A. MCCAULAY and A. P. LIEN, *J. Amer. Chem. Soc.*, 1951, **73**, 2013.
9. L. J. ANDREWS and R. M. KEEFER, *J. Amer. Chem. Soc.*, 1953, **75**, 3776.
10. M. ORCHIN, *J. Org. Chem.*, 1951, **16**, 1165; B. V. TRONOV *et al.*, *Tr. Tomskogo Gos. Univ., Ser. Khim.*, 1964, **170**, 180.
11. T. S. MOORE *et al.*, *J. Chem. Soc.*, 1931, 1447.
12. D. LL. HAMMICK and T. K. HANSON, *J. Chem. Soc.*, 1933, 669.
13. L. J. ANDREWS, *Chem. Revs.*, 1954, **54**, 752.
14. S. D. ROSS and I. KUNTZ, *J. Amer. Chem. Soc.*, 1954, **76**, 4176.
15. L. H. JONES and R. M. BADGER, *J. Amer. Chem. Soc.*, 1951, **73**, 3132.
16. M. TAMRES, *J. Amer. Chem. Soc.*, 1952, **74**, 3375.
17. E. J. BOWEN and E. COATES, *J. Chem. Soc.*, 1947, 105, 130.
18. S. YAMASHITA, *Bull. Univ. Osaka Prefect.*, Ser. A, 1959, **7**, 201.
19. W. A. G. GRAHAM and F. G. A. STONE, *J. Inorg. Nucl. Chem.*, 1956, **3**, 164.
20. E. WIBERG and U. HEUBAUM, *Z. anorg. Chem.*, 1935, **225**, 270; E. A. FLETCHER, Thesis, Purdue Univ., 1952.
21. D. R. MARTIN and R. DIAL, *J. Amer. Chem. Soc.*, 1950, **72**, 852.
22. A. STOCK, *Ber.*, 1901, **34**, 949.
23. A. W. LAUBENGAYER and D. S. SEARS, *J. Amer. Chem. Soc.*, 1945, **67**, 164.
24. W. G. BARB, *Trans. Faraday Soc.*; 1953, **49**, 143; E. R. GARRETT and R. L. GUILE, *J. Amer. Chem. Soc.*, 1953, **75**, 3958.
25. D. WILLIAMS, *Phys. Rev.*, 1936, **50**, 719; E. K. PLYLER and D. R. WILLIAMS, ibid., 1936, **49**, 215; W. GORDY and P. C. MARTIN, *J. Chem. Phys.*, 1939, **7**, 99; N. S. RAO and S. K. K. JATKAR, *Quart. J. Indian Inst. Sci.*, 1942, **5**, 65; id. ibid., 1942, **6**, 1.
26. L. J. ANDREWS and R. M. KEEFER, *J. Amer. Chem. Soc.*, 1951, **73**, 462.
27. A. F. KAPUSTINSKII and S. I. DRAKIN, *Izvest. Akad. Nauk SSSR, Odtel Khim. Nauk*, 1950, 233; K. SZCZEPANIAK and A. TRAMER, *Bul. Acad. Polon. Sci. Ser. Sci.*, 1965, **13**, 79.
28. R. E. RUNDLE and J. H. GORING, *J. Amer. Chem. Soc.*, 1950, **72**, 5337.
29. D. LL. HAMMICK *et al.*, *J. Chem. Soc.*, 1932, 1530.
30. H. KRONBERGER and J. WEISS, *J. Chem. Soc.*, 1944, 464; I. NITTA *et al.*, *Sci. Papers Osaka Univ.*, 1951, No. 29; M. CHOWDHURY, *Trans. Faraday Soc.*, 1961, **57**, 1482.
31. L. J. ANDREWS and R. M. KEEFER, *J. Amer. Chem. Soc.*, 1951, **73**, 4169.
32. L. FRIEDLIN *et al.*, *J. Gen. Chem. USSR*, 1939, **9**, 1589.
33. D. S. ACKER *et al.*, *J. Amer. Chem. Soc.*, 1960, **82**, 6408; R. G. KEPLER *et al.*, *Phys. Rev. Letters*, 1960, **5**, 503; D. B. CHESNUT *et al.*, *J. Chem. Phys.*, 1961, **34**, 684.
34. T. BJORVATTEN and O. HASSEL, *Acta Chem. Scand.*, 1959, **13**, 1261; O. HASSEL, *Svensk Kem. Tidskr.*, 1960, **72:2**, 88; O. HASSEL, *Tidskr. Kjemi*

*Bergvsen Met.*, 1961, **3**, 60: O. HASSEL, *Nature (London)*, 1961, **189**, 137; P. GROTH and O. HASSEL, *Proc. Chem. Soc.*, 1961, 343.
35. L. L. FERSTANDING *et al.*, *J. Amer. Chem. Soc.*, 1961, **83**, 1151.
36. M. CHOWDHURY, *J. Phys. Chem.*, 1961, **65**, 1899; J. CZEKALLA and K. O. MEYER, *Z. phys. Chem.*, 1961, **27**, 185; K. B. EINSENTHAL and M. A. EL-SAYED, *J. Chem. Phys.*, 1965, **42**, 794.
37. G. C. MARTIN and A. R. UBBELOHDE, *J. Chem. Soc.*, 1961, 4948, 4958.
38. M. FELDMAN and S. WINSTEIN, *J. Amer. Chem. Soc.*, 1961, **83**, 3338.
39. N. K. BRIDGE, *J. Chem. Phys.*, 1960, **32**, 945; S. J. RAND and R. L. STRONG, *J. Amer. Chem. Soc.*, 1960, **82**, 5; R. L. STRONG *et al*, ibid., 1960, **82**, 5053; R. L. STRONG and J. PERANO, ibid., 1961, **83**, 2843; G. PORTER and J. A. SMITH, *Proc. Roy. Soc. (London)*, 1961, **A262**, 476; L. J. ANDREWS and R. M. KEEFER, *Advances in Inorganic and Radiochemistry*, eds. EMELÉUS and SHARPE, Acad. Press, New York, 1961, vol. 3, pp. 91–131; E. K. MELLON and J. J. LAPOWSKI, *Nature (London)*, 1963, **199**, 997.
40. R. E. MERRIFIELD and W. D. PHILLIPS, *J. Amer. Chem. Soc.*, 1958, **80**, 2778; R. FOSTER and P. HANSON, *Tetrahedron*, 1965, **21**, 255; F. E. STEWART *et al.*, *J. Chem. Phys.*, 1966, **44**, 2866.
41. J. LANDAUER and H. MCCONNELL, *J. Amer. Chem. Soc.*, 1952, **74**, 1221.
42. D. LL. HAMMICK and A. HELLICAR, *J. Chem. Soc.*, 1938, 761.
43. G. BENNETT and R. L. WAIN, *J. Chem. Soc.*, 1936, 1108.
44. T. SINOMIYA, *Bull. Chem. Soc. Japan*, 1940, **15**, 92, 137, 281, 309.
45. H. LEY and P. PFEIFFER, *Ber. deut. Chem. Ges.*, 1921, **54**, 367; H. LEY and R. GRAU, ibid., 1925, **58**, 1765; R. E. GIBSON and O. H. LOEFFLER, *J. Amer. Chem. Soc.*, 1940, **62**, 1324.
46. A. B. BURG and A. A. GREEN, *J. Amer. Chem. Soc.*, 1943, **65**, 1838; N. V. SIDGWICK, *The Chemical Elements and their Compounds*, Clarendon Press, Oxford, 1950, p. 401; H. A. SKINNER, *Cationic Polymerization*, ed. P. H. PLESCH, Heffer, Cambridge, 1953, p. 35; R. S. NYHOLM, *Revs. Pure Appl. Chem.*, 1954, **4**, 15; G. E. COATES, *Organo-metallic Compounds*, Methuen, London, 1956, p. 62.
47. H. C. BROWN and R. R. HOLMES, *J. Amer. Chem. Soc.*, 1956, **78**, 2173.
48. P. R. HAMMOND, *Nature (London)*, 1965, **206**, 891.
49. R. S. MULLIKEN and W. B. PERSON, *Ann. Rev. Phys. Chem.*, 1962, **13**, 107.
50. A. H. MAKI and D. H. GERKE, *J. Amer. Chem. Soc.*, 1960, **82**, 2671.
51. G. A. RUSSELL *et al.*, *J. Amer. Chem. Soc.*, 1964, **86**, 1807.
52. R. L. WARD, *J. Chem. Phys.*, 1963, **39**, 852.
53. R. H. BOYD, *J. Chem. Phys.*, 1963, **38**, 2529.
54. T. L. CAIRNS *et al.*, *J. Amer. Chem. Soc.*, 1958, **80**, 2775; S. B. NEEDLEMAN and M. C. CHANG KUO, *Chem. Revs.*, 1962, **62**, 405; R. HUISGEN, *Angew. Chem. (Intern. Ed.)*, 1963, **2**, 565, 633.
55. A. H. MAKI and D. H. GERKE, *J. Amer. Chem. Soc.*, 1961, **83**, 1852.
56. P. R. HAMMOND, *J. Chem. Soc.*, 1964, 471; B. F. PLUMMER, Thesis, Ohio State Univ., Columbus, 1960.
57. G. F. CRABB and G L. KEARNS, *J. Phys. Chem.*, 1962, **66**, 436.
58. M. R. BASILA and D. J. CLANCY, *J. Phys. Chem.*, 1963, **67**, 1551.
59. E. W. STONE and A. H. MAKI, *J. Chem. Phys.*, 1963, **39**, 1635.
60. R. E. BUCKLES and J. F. MILLS, *J. Amer. Chem. Soc.*, 1953, **75**, 552.
61. H. MURAKAMI, *J. Chem. Phys.*, 1954, **22**, 367.
62. O. HASSEL, *Proc. Chem. Soc.*, 1957, 250; J. D. MCCULLOUGH *et al.*, *Acta Cryst.*, 1959, **12**, 815; P. J. HENDRA and N. SADASIVAN, *Spectrochim. Acta*, 1965, **21**, 1127.

63. J. D. McCULLOUGH and R. E. MARSH, *Acta Cryst.*, 1950, **3**, 41.
64. R. M. KEEFER and L. J. ANDREWS, *J. Amer. Chem. Soc.*, 1952, **74**, 1891.
65. J. THIELE and W. PETER, *Ber.*, 1905, **38**, 2842.
66. R. M. KEEFER and L. J. ANDREWS, *J. Amer. Chem. Soc.*, 1953, **75**, 543.
67. G. EIA and O. HASSEL, *Acta Chem. Scand.*, 1956, **10**, 139.
68. O. HASSEL, *Mol. Phys.*, 1958, **1**, 241.
69. O. HASSEL and C. RØMMING, *Acta Chem. Scand.*, 1956, **10**, 696.
70. J. A. A. KETELAAR and C. VAN DE STOLPE, *Rec. Trav. Chim.*, 1952, **71**, 805.
71. J. A. A. KETELAAR *et al.*, *Rec. Trav. Chim.*, 1952, **71**, 1104; G. KORTÜM and W. M. VOGEL, *Z. Elektrochem.*, 1955, **59**, 16; R. M. KEEFER and L. J. ANDREWS, *J. Amer. Chem. Soc.*, 1955, **77**, 2164; P. A. D. DeMAINE, *J. Chem. Phys.*, 1957, **26**, 1189, 1192, 1199; N. W. TIDESWELL and J. D. McCULLOUGH, *J. Amer. Chem. Soc.*, 1957, **79**, 1031.
72. E. COLTON, *J. Amer. Chem. Soc.*, 1955, **77**, 3211; S. NAGAKURA, ibid., 1958, **80**, 520.
73. N. OGIMACHI *et al.*, *J. Amer. Chem. Soc.*, 1955, **77**, 4202.
74. L. J. ANDREWS and R. M. KEEFER, *J. Amer. Chem. Soc.*, 1952, **72**, 805.
75. J. G. TRAYNHAM and J. R. OLECHOWSKI, *J. Amer. Chem. Soc.*, 1959, **81**, 571.
76. J. S. HAM *J. Chem. Phys.*, 1952, **20**, 1170; R. M. KEEFER and L. J. ANDREWS, *J. Amer. Chem. Soc.*, 1953, **75**, 3561; G. KORTÜM and M. KORTÜM-SEILER, *Z. Naturw.*, 1950, **5a**, 544.
77. A. I. POPOV and R. H. RYGG, *J. Amer. Chem. Soc.*, 1957, **79**, 4622.
78. R. N. HASZELDINE, *J. Chem. Soc.*, 1953, 1757.
79. A. TRAMER, *Bull. Acad. Polon. Sci.*, 1964, **12**, 669.
80. G. L. RYZHOVA *et al.*, *Zh. Obshch. Khim.*, 1965, **35**, 429.
81. Y. MATSUNAGA, *Nature (London)*, 1966, **211**, 182.

# CHAPTER 6

# MOLECULAR COMPLEXES OF GROUP III ELEMENTS OF THE PERIODIC TABLE

BORON, aluminium, and the other elements of Group III form a large number of molecular complexes with ligands of Groups V and VI, as well as with aromatic electron donors. While organic complexes dissociate readily and extensively, certain ligands of Groups V and VI give rise to a donor–acceptor bond of considerable polarity, so that the resulting product is not a true addition complex. However, a large number of complexes formed between boron, aluminium and sub-Group IIIb elements on one hand and ligands of Groups V and VI on the other are true molecular addition complexes, ranging from unstable to very stable entities with a well-marked gradation in properties, as shown in Table 6.1.

An extensive list of these complexes is given by Stone.[10] The most stable member of the series is $Me_3N–BF_3$, in which the nitrogen–boron dative bond is highly polar $Me_3\overset{+}{N}\overset{-}{B}F_3$. This tendency of boron and its congeners to form addition complexes with suitable donor molecules has been recognized for a considerable time. Indeed, Gay-Lussac[13] prepared the $H_3N–BF_3$ complex about 160 years ago, while Davy[14] subjected this addition complex to some detailed study. Strictly speaking, the $Me_3N–BF_3$ and similar complexes are not true addition molecular complexes, since they display a very strong donor–acceptor bond of considerable polarity. In the final analysis, however, these strongly polar complexes may be considered to belong to the class species for which the dative bond contribution is predominant in the wave equation [eqn.(2.1)].

TABLE 6.1. *Molecular complexes for Group III elements*

| Donor | Acceptor | $K_p$ (atm) at 373·2°K | $\Delta G°$ at 373·2°K (kcal/mole) | Ref. |
|-------|----------|------------------------|-----------------------------------|------|
| $NMe_3$ | $AlMe_3$ | Too stable to permit measurements in the gaseous phase | | 1 |
| $NMe_3$ | $BF_3$ | 4 | | 2 |
| $Me_2PH$ | $BF_3$ | 10·5 | −1·74 | 3 |
| $Me_2PH$ | $BMe_3$ | 9·8 | −1·69 | 3 |
| $NH_3$ | $BMe_3$ | 4·62 | −1·13 | 3,4 |
| $Me_3As$ | $GaMe_3$ | 1·34 | − | 5 |
| $Et_2NH$ | $BMe_3$ | 1·22 | −0·15 | 4,6 |
| $Me_3N$ | $BMe_3$ | 0·472 | 0·56 | 3,7 |
| $Me_2O$ | $BF_3$ | 0·18 | 1·25 | 8 |
| $Me_3P$ | $BF_3$ | 0·07 | 1·99 | 9 |
| $MeNH_2$ | $BMe_3$ | 0·04 | 2·47 | 5 |
| $Me_2NH$ | $AsMe_3$ | 0·02 | 2·88 | 3, 10,13 |
| $Me_3As$ | $InMe_3$ | Too highly dissociated to be measured | | 11 |
| $PH_3$ | $BMe_3$ | Not formed even at −78°C | | 12 |
| $Me_3Sb$ | $BF_3$ | Not formed even at −78°C | | 12 |

## *Interaction between Group III acceptor and Groups V or VI donors*

In general donor ligands of Group V form more stable adducts with Group III acceptors than the corresponding donor molecules of Group VI or VII elements. For example,[1] the observed decrease of donor power, i.e. order of co-ordination, follows the increase in nuclear charge on passing from Groups V to VII, viz. $Me_3N > Me_3O > Me_3F$ towards $Me_3B$, $BF_3$ or $B_2H_6$. There is also in most cases a definite gradation in properties within a group of complexes formed between donors of a given group and acceptors of another group; the co-ordinate link may in theory vary from incomplete sharing of the lone pair giving a weak bond, to nearly complete sharing with transfer of one electronic charge to the acceptor atom, giving a strong bond.

### Irreversible decomposition of molecular complex

Under appropriate conditions depending on the nature of the complex many molecular complexes decompose irreversibly with a loss of small molecules, e.g. molecular hydrogen, methane, etc. This decomposition is due to electrical strains set up in the molecule of the complex as a result of charge-transfer. For instance, when the ligand atom, which is electronegative relative to hydrogen, is bonded to the latter, charge-transfer from donor to acceptor increases the protonic character of the hydrogen still further; also since the electron density on groups of the acceptor atom becomes greater during this process, the elimination of hydrogen in this instance relieves these strains and stabilizes the rest of the complex. The actual conditions required to effect decomposition, which vary from low to very high temperatures and pressures, and the nature of the eliminated molecule depend on the nature of the complex. Thus addition complexes formed by boron halides or their organic derivatives with ligands containing hydrogen tend to lose hydrogen halide.[15] On the other hand, complexes formed by borane or its alkyl derivatives with ligands containing active hydrogen, e.g. dimethylamine or dimethylphosphine decompose on heating at moderate pressures with the evolution of hydrogen,[16] while aluminium trimethyl reacts with methanol to give methane,[1] and gallium trimethyl undergoes immediate reaction with the alcohol to give the dimeric methoxide, viz.

$$2GaMe_3 \xrightarrow[\text{MeOH}]{} (Me_2GaOMe)_2$$

Similar derivatives of gallium have been prepared from phenols, thiophenol, methanethiol and methaneselenol. These dimeric complexes are very stable and hardly dissociate into the monomers in the gaseous state, but some combine with electron pair donors,[17] e.g. $Me_3N$. In contrast to the above, the complex $(Me_2In \cdot SMe)_2$ or $(Me_2Tl \cdot SMe)_2$ do not react with $Me_3N$. In general the dimethylmetal derivatives $Me_2M^{III}R$, where $M$ is the tervalent metal of Group III (except boron), and $R$ is $Me_2N-$, $Me_2P-$, $MeO-$, $MeS-$, $MeSe-$, or $H_2N-$, are dimeric or trimeric while many of the corresponding boron derivatives are monomeric, e.g. $Me_2BNMe_2$. The monomeric boron complexes probably exist as a result of the boron–nitrogen or boron–oxygen $\sigma,\pi$-bond, since the lone-pair electrons on the donor atoms (oxygen or nitrogen) can react with the $2p_\pi$ orbital of boron owing to the absence of inner-shell repulsion.[18] It follows that if this type of repulsion is present, even the boron complexes will be polymeric. This is found to be the case, e.g. $Me_2BPMe_2$ is trimeric owing to the presence in the molecule of phosphorus, an element in the second row of the Periodic Table. The apparent exception of monomeric $Me_2BSMe$ is explained by noting that there is insufficient $S-B$ external dative bonding to effect polymerization, because the dative bonding power of sulphur is weaker than that of nitrogen or phosphorus.

An important application of these irreversible reactions is the preparation of a wide variety of synthetic complexes containing $B-N$, $B-P$, $Al-S$, $Al-P$, $Ga-N$, etc., bonds.[5, 15, 16, 19]

## Complexes of boron

The most stable molecular complex of boron is $BMe_3 \cdot BF_3$, because the highly electronegative fluorine increases the Lewis acidity of the acceptor atoms. Thus the corresponding enthalpy change for the gas-phase and liquid-phase dissociation is about $30\cdot9$ kcal/mole.[20] This is in accordance with Mulliken theory[21] (also see Chapter 2), since there is a complete transfer of an electron from $NMe_3$ to $BF_3$ (the second term of the wave equation predominates), giving the complex $Me_3\overset{+}{N}\overset{-}{B}F_3$, in which a bond is formed by the odd electron between $BF_3^-$ and $Me_3N^+$. The ability of a donor to transfer a lone-pair is sometimes reduced by any electron-attracting groups present. For example, the adduct $PF_3 \cdot BF_3$ has not been prepared, while $PH_3 \cdot BF_3$ exists.[9, 22] In many cases, however, these electronegativity considerations do not apply. For instance, $AsH_3 \cdot BF_3$ is known, whereas $H_3As \cdot BCl_3$ can be prepared.[23] This appears to apply to boron halide acceptors in the case of arsine,[23,24] $PCl_3$,[25] pyridine or nitrobenzene donors.[26] Similar considerations apply to alkyl borates[27] (H. A. Skinner and N. B. Smith, ref. 24) which are weak acceptors, though alkoxy groups are electronegative. It is probable that there is $\pi$-bonding between the oxygen lone-pair electrons and the $p_x$ orbital of boron, so that considerable energy is required to free that orbital for bonding. This view is supported by the observation that aryl borates form complexes with amines,[63] since the $p_\pi$–$p_\pi$ bond in the boron-oxygen link is weaker because of the presence of the electronegative phenyl groups (M. F. Lappert, ref. 19). The same considerations apply to boron halides $BX_3$, since $\pi$-bonding between B and X increases with the increasing atomic number of halogens, so that the acceptor power of boron is reduced.[26]

As far as the effect of the atomic number of the donor is concerned, the boron-trifluoride complexes of Group V and VI elements decrease in stability from nitrogen to antimony, and from oxygen to selenium, respectively. This is not, however, generally true for other boron compounds, e.g. alkyls. Thus the complex $PH_3 \cdot BMe_3$ does not exist, while $PMe_3 \cdot BMe_3$ and $NMe_3 \cdot BMe_3$ have about the same stability;[3, 7, 12, 28] on the other hand,[12] there is a large difference in stability between $NH_3 \cdot BMe_3$ and $PH_3 \cdot BMe_3$, whilst borane forms a more stable complex with $PMe_3$ than does boron trifluoride.[29] Indeed, borane behaves differently from other boron compounds by showing an order of co-ordination, $Me_3P > Me_3N \gg Me_3As > Me_3Sb$ (A. B. Burg and F. G. A. Stone, ref. 16), and it resembles in this respect gallium trimethyl; furthermore, borane is the only acceptor of Group III, which is able to combine with boron trifluoride or carbon monoxide but not with nitrogen trifluoride. The replacement of electron-releasing methyl groups by hydrogen atoms in borane results in a reduction of the acceptor power. For instance,[30] the enthalpy change of formation decreases from 31·5 kcal/mole for $NMe_3 \cdot BH_3$ to 17·6 kcal/mole for $NMe_3 \cdot BMe_3$; steric and hyperconjugation effects are probably responsible for the observed order of stability. Moreover, while borane forms a stable complex with trimethylamine, it does not combine with the silicon analogue $(SiH_3)_3N$, though silicon is more electropositive than carbon, i.e. it is more electron-releasing.[31] This weakness of trisilylamine as a donor is due to the fact that it cannot supply sufficient energy to break the B—H—B bond, because the silyl groups have electron-attracting power when bonded to electronegative atoms.[32] It follows that the order of donor potentiality towards an acceptor ought to be

$$(SiH_3)_3N < (SiH_3)_2MeN < (SiH_3) Me_2N < Me_3N$$

This has been found to be true to some extent in the case of boron trimethyl or trifluoride acceptors.[31,33] It is worth noting that similar considerations apply to the donor diethyl ether,[8,34] since $Et_2O \cdot BF_3$ does exist, while $Et_2O \cdot BMe_3$ and $Et_2O \cdot BH_3$ do not exist even at $-78°C$. On the other hand, a weak adduct $Et_2S \cdot BMe_3$ exists[20] because the S—B bond is longer than the O—B bond, so that there is less interference between the methyl groups on the components of the complex. This explanation is supported by the observation that for the boron trifluoride acceptor, where there is much less steric hindrance, the reverse order of stability is found for diethyl ether or diethyl sulphide.[8,29,34,35]

The importance of steric effects is also seen in the case of the etherates.[8] Thus $Me_2O \cdot BF_3$ is very much less stable than the tetrahydrofurane–boron trifluoride complex, although on the basis of inductive effects both should be of nearly equal stability; this steric hindrance does not exert, however, any effect in the case of borane, so that for this acceptor the order of co-ordination is:

$$Et_2O < Me_2O < C_4H_8O$$

as expected.[36]

There are other factors to be considered in the context of complex stability. Thus, while for boron trifluoride the order of co-ordination is

$$Me_2Se < Me_2S < Me_2O$$

as expected, it appears that for borane, which has lower steric requirements, the order is similar to that for trimethyl boron.[16,20,29,37] Also $Me_2S \cdot BF_3$ is much less stable than $Me_2S \cdot BH_3$. Similar considerations apply to nitrogen and phosphorus in Group V, when borane is used as an acceptor.

Various theories have been advanced to explain the abnormal behaviour of borane, but none appears to be entirely satisfactory[38] (see also F. G. A. Stone, ref. 10, p. 119). The most probable explanation is that the complexes of borane are stabilized by dative $\pi$-bonds when the donor atom is in the second or subsequent rows of the Periodic Table, where there is an empty $d$-orbital present. This, of course, is not possible in the case of the donor atom of the first row of the Periodic Table owing to the absence of $d$-orbital. This question is not settled yet, however.

### Boron trichloride–organic compounds interaction

A very important class of molecular complexes involving boron is that resulting from the interaction of boron trichloride with organic compounds. An extensive review of these complexes has been given by Gerrard and Lappert.[39]

Since boron trichloride is a powerful Lewis acid, it would be expected to react with organic functional groups containing oxygen, sulphur, nitrogen, phosphorus or halogens, as well as with olefins, acetylenes, aromatic hydrocarbons, organo-metallic and organo-metalloidal compounds. Thus, most organic compounds, with the exception of paraffins and cyclo-paraffins, will react with this powerful electrophilic agent. The nature of the equilibria involved and the products depends on the great strength of boron trichloride as a Lewis acid and on the high polarizability of the boron–chlorine bond, so that the compound is more versatile than the more reactive boron trifluoride, which forms a wide range of co-ordination complexes. In the case of boron trichloride, however, in addition to somewhat similar reactions,[40] the reaction with suitable donors proceeds via co-ordination complexes through a number of stages to a great variety of complex products.

Table 6.2 gives the salient features of the reactions between boron trichloride with various classes of organic compounds (in alphabetical order).

TABLE 6.2. *Reactions between* $BCl_3$ *and various organic compounds*

| Donor | Experimental conditions | Products of interaction | Remarks | Notes | Ref. |
|---|---|---|---|---|---|
| Acetylene | Catalyst ($Hg_2Cl_2$ or activated charcoal at 150°C) | $\beta$-chlorovinyl-borons ($ClCH=CH)_n BCl_{(3-n)}$ where $n = 1, 2$ or $3$ | Similar behaviour with $\alpha$-acetylenes | (a) | 41 |
| Acids (carboxy) and anhydrides | (i) e.g. excess acetic acid. (ii) e.g. acetic anhydrides | $[(CH_3CO_2)_2B]_2O$ $CH_3COCl$ | Other products obtained by varying the proportions of the reactants | (b) | 42 43 |
| Alcohols (ROH) (also see under ethylene glycol) | (i) In a sealed tube at $-80°C$ in $n$-pentane | $B(OR)_3$ (borates) | Quantitative yield from wide range of alcohols, except $C_6H_5CH_2OH$ and $C_6H_5MeCHOH$ | | 44 |
| | (ii) Prolonged heating with pyridine in chloroform solution. | $RCl$ (alkyl chlorides) | High yield and of general applicability | | 45 |
| | (iii) Equimolar proportions | $ROBCl_2$ (boronites) | Quantitative yield from wide range of alcohols except when alkyl groups are electron-releasing e.g. $CH_2=CH-CH_2$ | | 46 |
| | (iv) $1BCl_3 + 2ROH$ | $(RO)_2BCl$ (boronates) | | | |

TABLE 6.2. *Reactions between* $BCl_3$ *and various organic compounds* (continued)

| Donor | Experimental conditions | Products of interaction | Remarks | Notes | Ref. |
|---|---|---|---|---|---|
| Aldehydes (RCHO) | (i) with acetaldehyde or monochloro-acetaldehyde | $(RCHCl)_2O$ α-chloro-ether | Nature of products of reaction with ketones is uncertain | (c) | 47 |
| | (ii) Reaction with di- or trichloro acetaldehyde even at $-80°C$ | $B(OCHClR)_3$ α-chloro-alkyl borate | | | |
| Amines | (i) Primary amines in benzene at $-15°C$, e.g. $p$-toluidine or $p$-anisidine | In general, 1:1 complex results, but dodecylamine gives a range of addition products | On heating HCl is evolved and a substituted borazole is formed | | 48 |
| | (ii) Secondary amines in $n$-pentane solution or in a vacuum, e.g. $Me_2NH$ (1:1) | $Me_2NBCl_2$ and HCl evolved | Nature of products depend on proportions of reactants. HCl formed reacts with amine and complex hence the low yield of the latter | | 49 |
| | (iii) Tertiary amines (several aliphatic, aromatic and heterocyclic) | 1:1 complexes | Aromatic amines undergo dimerization owing to steric effects | | 50 |
| | (iv) Quarternary salts, e.g. $Me_4NCl$ | Substituted borazole | Exceptionally stable. Also complex formation in benzene solution Very stable complex | | 51 |

144

| Donor | Experimental conditions | Products of interaction | Remarks | Notes | Ref. |
|---|---|---|---|---|---|
| Benzene | Catalyst-palladium black at 500–600°C | $C_6H_5BCl_2$ Phenylboron dichloride | High yield | | 52 |
| Chloride | (i) acyl, e.g. $CH_3COCl$ | 1 : 1 complex | None with benzoyl chloride | | 53 |
| | (ii) alkyl, e.g. $(C_6H_5)_3CCl$ | 1 : 1 complex | Moderately stable complex | (d) | 54 |
| Dioxane | Any proportion | 1 : 1 complex | Other cyclic ethers behave similarly | | 55 |
| Esters (carboxylic) (RCOOR') | Moderate conditions | Fairly stable complex | Decomposes on heating (fission of alkyl–oxygen or acyl–oxygen. Alkyl–oxygen fission occurs if R' is a secondary tertiary alkyl group) | | 56 |
| Ethers (also see under dioxane) | (i) Aliphatic ($R_2O$); rapid formation at −80°C | $R_2O \cdot BCl_3$ | On heating to 56°C $ROBCl_2$ is obtained | (e) | 57 |
| | (ii) Cyclic, including tetrahydrofuran and tetrahydropyran, in equimolecular proportions | 1 : 1 complex | No reaction with cyclic monoethers owing to I strain | | 58 |

145

TABLE 6.2. *Reactions between* $BCl_3$ *and various organic compounds* (continued)

| Donor | Experimental conditions | Products of interaction | Remarks | Notes | Ref. |
|---|---|---|---|---|---|
| Ethylene glycol (also see under alcohols) | Nature of product depends on proportions of reactants | $(CH_2O_2BCl$, or $Cl_2BO(CH_2)_2$ $OBCl_2$ or $(CH_2O)_2BO(CH_2)_2OH$ | Products of reaction with propylene and butylene glycol (1:1 proportions) are used for synthesizing cyclic boron complexes | | 59 |
| Nitriles | e.g. with acetonitrile in benzene at $-80°C$ | 1:1 complex | Solid complex having the structure $RC \equiv N:BCl_3$ | | 60 |
| Nitro-compounds | Mild conditions | $C_6H_5NO_2 \cdot BCl_3$ | Dissociates on heating | (f) | 61 |
| $\alpha$-olefins | Gaseous-phase reaction | Polymer of the olefin | $BCl_3$ less efficient as a catalyst than $BF_3$ | | 62 |
| Phenols | (i) $ArOH - 1:1$ proportion at $-70°C$ in methylene chloride | $ArOBCl_2$ | Rapid reaction and quantitative yield; on adding more ArOH a rapid dechlorination occurs till $B(OAr)_3$ | | 63 |
| | (ii) Resorcinol, quinol or pyrogallol in 1:1 proportions | Polymerization, especially on heating | Products of reaction used for synthesizing cyclic boron complex | | 39 (p. 1090) 59 (J. A. Blau *et al.*) |

146

*Notes*

(a) The reaction between boron trichlorides and alcohols may be used for the preparation of a variety of more complex boron compounds than those shown in Table 6.2. The stepwise alkoxylation of the boron atom in $BCl_3$ may be viewed either as a $S_N2$ replacement or as a broadside four-centre approach of the reagent (cf. Gerrard and Lappert, ref. 50).

(b) The reaction sequence is complicated by interactions between the formed anhydrides and acyl chlorides with boron trichlorides.

(c) While aliphatic aldehydes and their chloro-derivatives react with boron trichloride, cyclic acetals and ketals of hexitols[64] are degraded by $BCl_3$.

(d) There is no reaction with alkyl chlorides in a wide temperature range, except perhaps with ethyl or isopropyl chloride.[65]

(e) Boron trichloride in benzene solution has zero dipole moment, but in ether solution its dipole moment is considerable[66] ($5 \cdot 89D$) (see also W. Nespital, ref. 60). This and other evidence points to the existence of a tetrahedral 1:1 complex. There is no reaction, however, between boron trichloride and diaryl ethers, probably due to their low basic strength,[67] but mixed arylalkyl ethers give aryloxyboron complexes.[68] Mixed dialkyl or diallyl ethers give alkyloxy (or allyloxy) boron complexes[69] (W. Gerrard *et. al.*, ref. 44). The reaction of boron trichloride with more complex ethers can be used for preparing many synthetic complexes (ref. 39, p. 1093), but fission of mixed ethers ROR' always leads to simple esters[68] via carbonium-ion formation ($S_N1$).

(f) Boron trifluoride does not react with nitrobenzene, while the trichloride does so under mild conditions. On heating, the 1:1 $C_6H_5 \cdot NO_2 - BCl_3$ complex dissociates, so that the formation and dissociation of the interaction product can be used to purify boron trichloride.

(g) An interesting case is that of the reaction between diborane and boron trichloride.[70] In the absence of ethers, no reaction occur. In the presence of ethers, however, the following reactions take place very readily with the production of chloroborane etherates

$$B_2H_6 + BCl_3 + 3R_2O \rightarrow 3H_2ClB \cdot OR_2 \qquad (a)$$

and

$$B_2H_6 + 4BCl_3 + 6R_2O \rightarrow 6HCl_2B \cdot OR_2. \qquad (b)$$

Boron trichloride also reacts with sodium or potassium boro-hydrides in the presence of ethers to give the product of reaction (a) the reaction being

$$MBH_4 + BCl_3 + 2R_2O \rightarrow 2H_2ClB \cdot OR_2,$$

where $M$ is Na or K. The product of reaction (b) is given by the reaction

$$MBH_4 + 3BCl_3 + 4R_2O \rightarrow 4HCl_2B \cdot OR_2 + MCl.$$

Hence diborane is produced in low yield from borohydrides in presence of boron trichloride and ethers. Furthermore, the chloroborane etherates react with olefins to form organoboranes; they also serve to reduce keto- but not carbonyl CO groups.

### Boron trifluoride molecular complexes

The molecular complexes formed by boron trifluoride with a variety of organic and inorganic donors have attracted great attention for over a hundred years because of the marked cataly-tic activity of the interaction products in particular, and of the acid–base and valency problems involved. The stability of those complexes is enormous,[71] ranging from highly unstable species, such as boron trifluoride–carbonyl chloride, which dissociates in the gas phase even at about $-130°$ C, to the extremely stable boron trifluoride–pyridine adduct which can be distilled without decom-position at $300°$ C.[71] In general,[35] only seven elements appear to be capable of forming molecular complexes with boron trifluoride and they all lie in the upper right-hand corner of the Periodic Classification: N, P, O, S, F, Cl and H. On the other hand, many simple inorganic compounds containing the above donor atoms do not co-ordinate to the acceptor owing to the interplay of various factors, such as the state of aggregation and stoichiometry, chemical nature of the donor molecular, steric effects, etc. For instance, all alkali sulphates, with the exception of lithium sulphate, form complexes with boron trifluoride; alkaline-earth metals and silver sulphate do not co-ordinate to the halide.[72] A large number of inorganic compounds containing potential donor atoms show very little tendency to form complexes with boron trifluoride, e.g. $P_2O_5$ or $I_2O_5$,[72] $AsH_3$,[73] $SOCl_2$ or $SO_2Cl_2$,[74] $N_2O$,[75] $CO$[76] and many others.

As far as the organic donors are concerned, the paraffin, olefin and aromatic hydrocarbons and their halogen derivatives, with the exception of triphenylmethyl fluoride, do not form complexes with the boron-trifluoride acceptor.[75,76,77] The reactivity of acyl halides except acetyl fluoride, and of benzoyl chloride or toluene–$p$-sulphonyl chloride is negligible;[53,78] the same considerations apply to certain ethers, e.g. glycol acetal or diphenyl oxide,[79] acid anhydrides with the exception of simple acid anhydrides and possibly of phthalic and succinic anhydrides;[53,79,80] $\beta$-diketones,[81] certain alcohols,[79,82] and Grignard reagents and other organo-metallic compounds[83] do not form complexes with boron trifluoride, though they react with it. Thus Grignard reagents yield trialkyl boron compounds, while $\beta$-diketones yield difluorides. The halide also reacts without complex formation with alkali and alkaline-earth metals,[84] with aluminium chloride and bromide,[85] and with oxides and certain oxysalts of elements of Groups I–IV of the Periodic Table.[86]

The factors affecting the stability of boron trifluoride complexes are as follows: stoichiometry, states of aggregation, steric effects and nature of the donor.

## 1. Stoichiometry

The 1:2 (1 acceptor–2 donor) complexes are generally more stable in the case of acidic or alcoholic donors.[82,87] It is worth noting that only about twenty complexes of the 1:2 type are known, whereas over two hundred 1:1 species have been prepared. In addition, the donors in the 1:2 complexes are usually those which form associated liquids, e.g. alcohols or acids, while in the case of monocomplexes the donors are of the type $R_2O$, $R_3N$ or $RCO_2R'$, i.e. compounds which are not associated.[82]

It follows that hydrogen bonding is of importance in determining the stability of 1:2 complexes.

Another explanation in terms of oxonium compounds[88] is based on the idea that the additional molecules of the donor may "solvate" the proton of the 1:1 interaction product and thus lead to the formation of a stable 1:2 complex. For example, the proton acid $HBF_4$ or $H^+BF_4^-$ (fluoroboric acid) cannot be isolated in the pure state; it can,[89] however, be stabilized to some extent by the addition of a further molecular of hydrogen fluoride to give $BF_3 \cdot 2HF$ or $H_2F^+BF_4^-$, which can be isolated as a solid[89] melting at about 57°C. In addition the second addend may be a molecule different from the first donor. For example, fluoroboric acid yields a stable complex by reaction with ammonia gas, so that the complex $BF_3 \cdot HF \cdot NH_3$, i.e. $NH_4^+BF_4^-$ is formed—a stable onium salt.[90] Another example concerns hydrogen fluoride and hexamethyl benzene;[91] the substituted aromatic compound will not mix with liquid hydrogen fluoride, but if gaseous boron trifluoride is stirred into the liquid, complete miscibility occurs owing to the formation of $BF_3 \cdot HF \cdot C_6Me_6$, i.e. $Me_6C_6H^+BF_4^-$. This phenomenom is quite general and about twenty ternary 1:1:1 complexes have been prepared.[91,92]

## 2. State of aggregation

In general, the stability of molecular complexes is frequently due to crystal-lattice energy in the solid state or solvation effects in the liquid state; the stability in the gaseous state is generally considerably lower than that in the liquid or solid states, and most boron trifluoride complexes are dissociated in the vapour phase. Indeed, the "boiling point" of these complexes is an unsatisfactory means of characterizing the species. Even complexes which distil unchanged may be highly dissociated in the vapour phase, though a few exceptions are known,[2] e.g. $BF_3–NH_2Me$, which is monomeric and undissociated at the boiling point. It is worth noting that the complexes of boron trifluoride with inorganic compounds all dissociate completely before boiling.[35,93] On the other hand, the stability of gaseous boron trifluoride complexes with organic compounds is usually greater than that of the inorganic equivalent, though it also depends considerably on the state of aggregation.[8]

## 3. Steric effects

The work of H. C. Brown and co-workers has drawn attention to the effect of steric strain on the stability of boron complexes. For instance, the stability of the ether complexes of boron trifluoride[8] may be represented by the series.

$$BF_3-C_4H_8O > BF_3-Me_2O > BF_3-Et_2O > BF_3-Pr_2O(i),$$

where $C_4H_8O$ is tetrahydrofuran and $Pr_2O(i)$ is isopropyl ether. Here steric effects are of primary importance in determining the stability of the complexes. Another example concerns the hydrides of Group V elements acting as donors (D. R. Martin and R. E. Dial, ref. 23). Thus boron trifluoride forms a complex with ammonia of phosphine but not with arsine while arsine coordinates to boron trichloride or tribromide. In this case other factors apart from steric considerations are also of importance. However, in the case of the nitriles, e.g. benzonitrile, o-toluonitrile and mesitonitrile, steric effects are slight, since the nitrile group is linear (ref. 73, p. 2934).

## 4. Nature of the donor

The stability of the molecular complexes of boron trifluoride is influenced by the nature of the donor element and the functional group containing it. The elements, which act as donors are N, P, O, S, F, Cl and H, all situated in the upper right-hand corner of the Periodic Table. The most important of these elements are nitrogen, oxygen and fluorine, which occur in the majority of the boron trifluoride complexes.

The functional group containing the donor atom also affects the stability of the complexes. For instance, complexes containing amines are usually more stable than those linked to substituted acid amides or nitriles. In this connection, one must note that electronegative substituents decrease the stability of complexes. For example, the order of decreasing stability for some oxygen donors.[53, 79, 94]

$$BF_3-Et_2O > BF_3-PhOEt > BF_3-Ph_2O.$$

Diphenyl oxide does not form a complex at all, phenetole

forms a complex that decomposes on warming, while the ethyl ether adduct is very stable. Since steric effects are known to be negligible in this case, it is clear that the replacement of ethyl groups by phenyl groups brings about a decrease in stability. Other examples showing the effect of polar substituents in the donor moiety are the chloro-substituted acetic acids, crotonic acid, oxalic acid, and chloroethanol complexes of boron trifluoride;[82] the trisilylamine and trimethylamine adducts[31] are of interest, since the latter is much more stable than the former.

### Structure of boron trifluoride complexes

The structures of these molecular complexes have been investigated by a variety of methods depending on the state of aggregation of the species (for additional methods see Chapter 3, pp. 43–52).

(a) *Solid state.* The structures of solid molecular complexes of boron trifluoride have been studied by infrared and Raman spectrophotometry, X-ray diffraction analysis and microscopy. For instance, the infrared spectra of ammonium fluoroborate[95] show that hydrogen in the complex does not appreciably affect the $B-F$ bonds and that the anion can be formulated as $BF_4^-$. It appears that X-ray diffraction analysis supports this view.[95, 96] On the other hand, there is no evidence of hydrogen bonding in the series of complexes of boron trifluoride with ammonia, methylamine, trimethylamine, and acetonitrile.[97] In addition, the donor molecule is less affected by complex formation than the acceptor molecule, while in the stable complex the bond length is shorter than that in the unstable variety. Some of the structural problems of the alkali fluoroborates and other complexes have also been investigated by microscopic techniques.

The solid 1 : 1 complexes of boron trifluoride (and other boron halides) with trimethylamine[108] have also been studied by isotopic shifts, using $^{11}B$ and $^{10}B$.

(b) *Liquid state.* The liquid complexes have been investigated by spectroscopy, thermal analysis and electrical conductance techniques. Thus, while the specific conductance of liquid boron trifluoride is negligible and that of the free donor liquids, such as dioxane water, alcohols, acids, esters, phenols, etc., is also very small (*ca.* $10^{-6}$ mhos/cm), the molten complexes have quite appreciable conductances, ranging from about $2 \cdot 8 \times 10^{-4}$ mhos/cm for $BF_3-Et_3N$ to $5 \cdot 82 \times 10^{-2}$ mhos/cm for $BF_3-2H_2O$.[93,98] Studies of Phase rule and colligative properties have also been applied in this field and some valuable information has been obtained concerning the composition of numerous complexes [73,75,77,79,91,98,99] (see also D. R. Martin and J. P. Faust, ref. 71). Extensive use has also been made of ultraviolet, infrared and Raman spectra to study the nature of the interaction products between donors and acceptors.[99,100] The ionization of molten complexes has been studied by electrolysis of the molten species[101] (see also ref. 35, pp. 13–14), the results show that these complexes ionize in many cases into ions quite different from those formed in organic solvents.[102]

(c) *Gaseous state.* The study of gaseous boron trifluoride complexes is difficult because of the extensive thermal dissociation in the vapour phase. Hence very few gaseous complexes have been investigated. One of the few is the $BF_3-Me_2O$ complex which has been studied by electron-diffraction techniques.[103]

### *Boron trifluoride complexes as catalysts*

The marked tendency of boron trifluoride to form molecular complexes depends upon the small molecular volume of the halide and upon the high electro-polarity and the unsaturated character of the boron atom. The compound forms complexes with most varied organic and inorganic compounds, and many of the products of interaction have high stability, e.g. the complex of boron trifluoride and pyridine dissociates only at temperatures above 300° C, while the ethyl etherate distils at 124° C at atmospheric pressure (P. D. van der Meulen and H. A. Heller, ref. 71). The high catalytic activity of the fluoride depends upon its great tendency to form complexes in which some intramolecular bonds are weakened and interatomic distances are increased, so that the organic moieties in the complexes become activated and enter into chemical reactions; the high catalytic activity of the halide itself probably depends upon its power to complex with organic compounds which contain unsaturated carbon atoms or elements capable of displaying their high valency.[104]

## Complexes of aluminium

In general the stability of the complexes formed between dimeric aluminium alkyl acceptors and the elements of Group V acting as donors is so great that there is hardly any dissociation in the gaseous phase.[1] For instance, the complex $Me_3N \cdot AlMe_3$ has a well-defined melting point at 105° C and boiling point at 177° C; the enthalpy change at the boiling point is 10·9 kcal/mole, and it is difficult to study the thermodynamics of the gaseous complex. Similarly, it is impossible to prepare organo-aluminium compounds by the Grignard method because of the great stability of the etherates (oxygen donor of Group VI) of aluminium trialkyls. This stability is further increased by replacing the alkyl groups of aluminium trialkyls by chlorine, as expected from theoretical considerations.

As far as the effect of the donor is concerned, there is an increase in stability of the complex with the decreasing atomic number of the donor atom. For example, the replacement reaction

$$NMe_3 + Me_3P \cdot AlMe_3 \rightleftharpoons PMe_3 + Me_3N \cdot AlMe_3$$

will proceed quantitatively to the right, while for Group VI donors the order of co-ordination is Te < Se < S < O. The replacement of methyl groups in the donor moiety by hydrogen reduces the stability of the complex, e.g. $Me_2PH \cdot AlMe_3$ is appreciably dissociated at 150° C, while $PMe_3 \cdot AlMe_3$ is not, for methyl groups in the donor moiety increase, in general, the stability of the complexes formed, provided that the steric effect is not appreciable, as already observed in the case of the acceptor.[3, 12, 28]

An interesting case is that of the reaction of aluminium trichloride with benzoyl chloride.[109] A study of the radioactive chlorine exchange between the two moieties showed that the complex has the ionic structure $[C_6H_5C = O]^+[AlCl_4]^-$ and not a dative structure, as previously thought.

### Complexes of Group IIIB acceptors

As already observed in the case of aluminium, the stability of the complexes incorporating gallium, indium and thallium decreases with increasing atomic number of the donor atoms.[105] For example, the order of stability of complexes formed between gallium trimethyl and Group V donors is N > P > As > Sb > Bi. Indeed, bismuth trimethyl does not form a complex with gallium trimethyl even at low temperatures, while $MMe_3 \cdot TlMe_3$ complexes in which M is N, P or As, are highly unstable.

As far as the acceptor species is concerned, the co-ordination order towards $NMe_3$ is Tl < In < Ga. Oddly enough, boron falls between indium and thallium — possibly because of steric effects. The interplay between the reluctance of electropositive metals to accept partial negative charges and the size of the acceptor atoms is clearly of importance. In the case of boron, the steric effect is at a maximum, since this element is the smallest of the Group, i.e. the N–B bond is the shortest of the N–$M$ bonds; on the other hand, boron is the least electropositive element of Group III. An additional factor is that connected with the presence of methyl groups on the acceptor moiety, since their electron-releasing property depends on the nature of the Group III atom to which they are attached. Hence this factor would tend to strengthen $NMe_3 \cdot GaMe_3$ relative to $NMe_3 \cdot BMe_3$.

The problem of complexes formed between the Group IIIB acceptors and Group VI elements is slightly different from that described above. With gallium trimethyl the order of co-ordination, i.e. stability,[5] is O > Se > S = Te, while in the case of aluminium the order was O > S > Se > Te. Two effects are responsible for the different behaviour of the gallium adduct. Firstly, gallium has a filled penultimate $d$-shell, so that these electrons can be used in $\pi$-bonding with empty low-energy orbitals, i.e. $d_\pi$–$d_\pi$ interaction occurs; this, of course, is not possible in the case of aluminium, which has no $d$-electrons. The second effect (G. E. Coates, loc. cit.) is connected with the increased tendency of Group VI elements to form dative $\pi$ bonds, as their atomic number increases. The first effect is very much stronger than the second in the case of Group V elements, so that the order of stability is $N > P > As > Sb > Bi$; while that of Group VI is $O > Se > S = Te$, as seen previously. There is also probably an entropy effect[17] which combined with the other effects described above would lead to the observed co-ordination sequence for the Group VI donors.

As regards the effect of the acceptor elements, there is a decrease in stability on passing from gallium to thallium acceptors when combined with Group VI donors, similar to the case of Group V elements. It is worth noting that surprisingly it is impossible at present to correlate ionization potentials of the donor atoms with the donor powers in Groups V or VI, even when the proton with its very slight steric requirements is the reference acceptor. Hence the length of the metal acceptor-ligand donor bond, i.e. the size of the ligand atoms, is of dominating importance though the donor power should normally increase with decreasing ionization potentials of the lone-pair electrons. This would lead to a minimum of donor power for the first row of elements in the Periodic Table relative to other rows, since their ionization potentials are the Group maximum — this, however, is contrary to experiment. On the other hand, the ionization potentials increase from nitrogen to oxygen, so that the order of co-ordination is $Me_3N > Me_2O$, as found. This contradiction may be partly due to the lack of precise data on ionization potentials, since their precise values depend on whether they are determined by photo-ionization[106] or electron-impact,[107] and partly to the above-mentioned effects of the size of the ligand atom.

## References

1. N. DAVIDSON and H. C. BROWN, *J. Amer. Chem. Soc.*, 1942, **64**, 316.
2. A. B. BURG and A. A. GREEN, *J. Amer. Chem. Soc.*, 1943, **65**, 1838.
3. H. C. BROWN, *J. Chem. Soc.*, 1956, 1248.
4. H. C. BROWN et al., *J. Amer. Chem. Soc.*, 1944, **66**, 435.
5. G. E. COATES, *J. Chem. Soc.*, 1951, 2003.
6. M. D. TAYLOR, *J. Amer. Chem. Soc.*, 1947, **69**, 1332.
7. H. C. BROWN et al., *J. Amer. Chem. Soc.*, 1944, **66**, 431.
8. H. C. BROWN and R. M. ADAMS, *J. Amer. Chem. Soc.*, 1943, **65**, 2557.
9. E. A. FLETCHER, Thesis, Purdue Univ., 1952.
10. F. G. A. STONE, *Chem. Revs.*, 1958, **58**, 101.
11. R. A. WHITCOMBE, *J. Chem. Soc.*, 1956, 335.

12. H. C. BROWN and R. H. HARRIS, Thesis, Purdue Univ., 1952.
13. J. GAY-LUSSAC, *Mémoires de la Société d'Arcueil*, 1809, **2**, 211.
14. H. DAVY, *Phil. Trans.*, 1812, **30**, 365.
15. A. B. BURG and R. I. WAGNER, *J. Amer. Chem. Soc.*, 1953, **75**, 3872.
16. A. B. BURG, *Rec. Chem. Progress, Kresge-Hooker Sci. Lib.*, 1954, **15**, 159; F. G. A. STONE, *Quart. Revs. (London)*, 1955, **9**, 174.
17. G. E. COATES and R. G. HAYTER, *J. Chem. Soc.*, 1953, 2519.
18. R. S. MULLIKEN, *J. Amer. Chem. Soc.*, 1950, **72**, 4493; K. S. PITZER, ibid., 1948, **70**, 2140.
19. E. WIBERG, *Naturw.*, 1948, **35**, 182, 212; O. C. MUSGRAVE, *J. Chem. Soc.*, 1956, 4305; M. F. LAPPERT, *Chem. Revs.*, 1956, **56**, 959.
20. W. A. G. GRAHAM and F. G. A. STONE, *J. Inorg. Nucl. Chem.*, 1956, **3**, 164.
21. R. S. MULLIKEN, *J. Amer. Chem. Soc.*, 1952, **74**, 811.
22. E. WIBERG and U. HEUBAUM, *Z. anorg. Chem.*, 1935, **225**, 270.
23. D. R. MARTIN and R. DIAL, *J. Amer. Chem. Soc.*, 1950, **72**, 852; A. STIEBER, *Compt. Rend.*, 1932, **195**, 610.
24. A. STOCK, *Ber.*, 1901, **34**, 949; H. A. SKINNER and N. B. SMITH, *J. Chem. Soc.*, 1954, 2324.
25. H. C. BROWN and R. R. HOLMES, *Abst. Papers, 129th Meeting, Amer. Chem. Soc.*, Cleveland, 1956, p. 28.
26. H. C. BROWN and R. R. HOLMES, *J. Amer. Chem. Soc.*, 1956, **78**, 2173.
27. H. C. BROWN and E. A. FLETCHER, *J. Amer. Chem. Soc.*, 1951, **73**, 2808.
28. S. SUJISHI, Thesis, Purdue Univ., 1949.
29. W. A. G. GRAHAM and F. G. A. STONE, *Chem. and Ind.*, 1956, 319.
30. H. I. SCHLESINGER *et al.*, *J. Amer. Chem. Soc.*, 1939, **61**, 1078.
31. A. B. BURG and E. S. KULJIAN, *J. Amer. Chem. Soc.*, 1950, **72**, 3103.
32. F. G. A. STONE and D. SEYFERTH, *J. Inorg. Nucl. Chem.*, 1955, **1**, 112.
33. S. SUJISHI and S. WITZ, *J. Amer. Chem. Soc.*, 1954, **76**, 4631.
34. A. W. LAUBENGAYER and G. R. FINLAY, *J. Amer. Chem. Soc.*, 1943, **65**, 884.
35. N. N. GREENWOOD and R. L. MARTIN, *Quart. Revs. (London)*, 1954, **8**, 1.
36. B. RICE *et al.*, *J. Amer. Chem. Soc.*, 1955, **77**, 2750.
37. H. I. SCHLESINGER and A. B. BURG, *J. Amer. Chem. Soc.*, 1938, **60**, 290.
38. D. H. MCDANIEL, *Science*, 1954, **125**, 545.
39 W. GERRARD and M. F. LAPPERT, *Chem. Revs.*, 1958, **58**, 1081.
40. D. R. MARTIN, *Chem. Revs.*, 1944, **44**, 461.
41. H. R. ARNOLD, U.S. Patent, 2, 402, 589, 1946; 2,402, 589 ·
42. W. GERRARD and M. A. WHEELANS, *Chem. and Ind.*, 1954, 758.
43. G. GUSTAVSON, *Ber.*, 1870, **3**, 426.
44. W. GERRARD *et al.*, *J. Chem. Soc.*, 1956, 3285; E. W. ABEL *et al.*, ibid., 1957, 501.
45. W. GERRARD and M. F. LAPPERT, *Chem. and Ind.*, 1952, 53; P. B. BRINDLEY, *J. Chem. Soc.*, 1956, 1540.
46. M. F. LAPPERT, *J. Chem. Soc.*, 1956, 1708.
47. M. J. FRAZER *et al.*, *J. Chem. Soc.*, 1957, 739; L. SUMMERS, *Chem. Revs.*, 1955, **55**, 301; N. W. SIDGWICK, *The Chemical Elements and their Compounds*, Oxford Univ. Press, London, 1950, p. 408.
48. S. J. GROSZOS and S. F. STAFIEF, *J. Amer. Chem. Soc.*, 1958, **80**, 1357; F. J. SOWA, U.S. Patent, 1953; 2, 655, 524; C. R. KINNEY and C. L. MAHONEY, *J. Org. Chem.*, 1943, **8**, 526.

49. W. GERRARD et al., J. Chem. Soc., 1957, 381; E. WIBERG and K. SCHUSTER, Z. anorg. allgem. Chem., 1933, **213**, 77.

50. F. GALLAIS and J. P. LAURENT, Compt. Rend., 1957, **244**, 1636; C. M. BAX et al., J. Chem. Soc., 1958, 1254, 1258; W. GERRARD and M. F. LAPPERT, ibid., 1951, 1020, 2545.

51. H. J. EMELÉUS and G. T. VIDELA, Proc. Chem. Soc., 1957, 288.

52. E. PACE, Atti Acad. Lincei, 1929, **10**, 193.

53. H. MEERWEIN and H. MEIER-HÜSER, J. prakt. Chem., 1932, **134**, 51.

54. E. WIBERG and U. HEUBAUM, Z. anorg. allgem. Chem., 1935, **222**, 98.

55. T. J. LANE et al., J. Amer. Chem. Soc., 1942, **64**, 2076.

56. M. J. FRAZER and W. GERRARD, J. Chem. Soc., 1955, 2959; W. GERRARD and M. H. WHEELANS, ibid., 1956, 4296.

57. L. GATTERMAN, Ber., 1889, **22**, 186.

58. J. D. EDWARDS et al., J. Chem. Soc., 1957, 348.

59. J. A. BLAU et al., J. Chem. Soc., 1957, 4116; L. HARTMAN, ibid., 1957, 1918; G. W. CONKLIN and R. R. MORRIS, Brit. Patent, 1958; 790,090.

60. A. W. LAUBENGAYER and D. S. SEARS, J. Amer. Chem. Soc., 1945, **67**, 164; W. NESPITAL, Z. phys. Chem., 1932, **B16**, 153.

61. R. C. JONES and C. R. KINNEY, J. Amer. Chem. Soc., 1939, **61**, 1378.

62. K. W. PEPPER, Quart. Revs. (London), 1954, **8**, 88.

63. T. COLCLOUGH et al., J. Chem. Soc., 1956, 3006.

64. S. ALLEN et al., Chem. and Ind., 1958, 630.

65. F. HEWITT and A. K. HOLLIDAY, J. Chem. Soc., 1953, 530.

66. H. ULICH and W. NESPITAL, Z. Elektrochem., 1931, **37**, 559.

67. T. COLCLOUGH et al., J. Chem. Soc., 1955, 907.

68. W. GERRARD and M. F. LAPPERT, J. Chem. Soc., 1952, 1486.

69. J. D. EDWARDS et al., J. Chem. Soc., 1957, 377.

70. H. C. BROWN and P. A. TIERNEY, J. Inorg. Nucl. Chem., 1959, **9**, 51.

71. P. A. VAN DER MEULEN and H. A. HELLER, J. Amer. Chem. Soc., 1932, **54**, 4404; D. R. MARTIN and J. P. FAUST, J. Phys. Colloid. Chem., 1949, **53**, 1255.

72. P. BAUMGARTEN and W. BRUNS, Ber., 1947, **80**, 517.

73. H. C. BROWN and R. B. JOHANNESEN, J. Amer. Chem. Soc., 1950, **72**, 852.

74. A. B. BURG and M. K. ROSS, J. Amer. Chem. Soc., 1943, **65**, 1637.

75. H. S. BOOTH and D. R. MARTIN, J. Amer. Chem. Soc., 1942, **64**, 2198.

76. V. GASSELIN, Ann. Chim. Phys., 1894, **3**, 5.

77. H. S. BOOTH and J. H. WALKUP, J. Amer. Chem. Soc., 1943, **65**, 2334.

78. F. SEEL, Z. anorg. Chem., 1943, **250**, 331.

79. H. BOWLUS and J. A. NIEUWLAND, J. Amer. Chem. Soc., 1931, **53**, 3855.

80. P. H. GIVEN and D. LL. HAMMICK, J. Chem. Soc., 1947, 1237.

81. G. T. MORGAN and R. B. TUNSTALL, J. Chem. Soc., 1924, **125**, 1963.

82. H. MEERWEIN and W. PANNWITZ, J. prakt. Chem., 1934, **141**, 123.

83. E. KRAUSE and R. N. NITSCHE, Ber., 1922, **55**, 1261; J. R. JOHNSON et al., J. Amer. Chem. Soc., 1938, **60**, 115; A. B. BURG, ibid., 1940, **62**, 2238.

84. S. G. RAWSON, Chem. News, 1888, **58**, 283.

85. E. L. GAMBLE et al., J. Amer. Chem. Soc., 1940, **62**, 1257.

86. P. BAUMGARTEN and W. BRUNS, Ber., 1941, **74**, 1232.

87. H. MEERWEIN, Ber., 1933, **66**, 411.

88. YA. M. PAUSHKIN, Zh. Priklad. Khim., 1948, **21**, 1199.

89. A. HANTZSCH, Ber., 1930, **63**, 1789.

90. J. J. GAY-LUSSAC and L. J. THENARD, Ann. Phys., 1809, **32**, 1.

91. D. A. McCaulay et al., Ind. Eng. Chem., 1950, 42, 2103; D. A. McCaulay and A. P. Lien, J. Amer. Chem. Soc., 1951, 73, 2013; id. ibid., 1952, 74, 6246.
92. H. C. Brown and H. Pearsall, J. Amer. Chem. Soc., 1951, 73, 4681; id. ibid., 1952, 74, 191; A. Schneider, ibid., 1952, 74, 2553; M. Kilpatrick and F. E. Luborsky, ibid., 1953, 75, 577; A. P. Lien et al., Ind. Eng. Chem., 1952, 44, 351; B. Ya. Rabinowich, J. Gen. Chem. USSR, 1951, 21, 71; G. Baddeley et al., J. Chem. Soc., 1952, 100; G. Williams and H. Bardsley, ibid., 1952, 1707; D. D. Eley and P. J. King, ibid., 1952, 2517, 4972; H. Meerwein, Angew. Chem., 1951, 63, 480.
93. J. H. de Boer and J. A. M. van Liempt, Rec. Trav. Chim., 1927, 46, 124; L. J. Klinkenberg, ibid., 1937, 56, 36; G. H. Curtis, Iron Age, 1945, 155, 54; N. N. Greenwood and R. L. Martin, J. Chem. Soc., 1951, 1915.
94. R. W. Dornte, U.S. Patent, 1951; 2,559,069.
95. G. L. Coté and H. W. Thompson, Proc. Roy. Soc.; 1951, A210, 217.
96. J. L. Hoard and V. Blair, J. Amer. Chem. Soc., 1935, 57, 1985.
97. J. L. Hoard et al., Acta Cryst., 1950, 3, 130; S. Geller and J. L. Hoard, ibid., 1950, 3, 121; J. L. Hoard et al., ibid., 1951, 4, 396; S. Geller and J. L. Hoard, ibid., 1951, 4, 399, 405.
98. J. S. McGrath et al., J. Amer. Chem. Soc., 1944, 66, 1263.
99. A. F. O. Germann and M. Cleaveland, Science, 1921, 63, 582; id., J. Phys. Chem., 1926, 30, 369; H. Gerding et al., Rec. Trav. Chim., 1952, 71, 501.
100. N. N. Greenwood and R. L. Martin, J. Phys. Chem., 1946, 50, 32; R. C. Osthoff and F. H. Clark, J. Amer. Chem. Soc., 1952, 74, 1361; E. L. Muetterties and E. G. Rochow, Z. anorg. Chem., 1952, 268, 221.
101. N. N. Greenwood et al., J. Chem. Soc., 1950, 3030.
102. R. L. Burwell and L. M. Elkin, J. Amer. Chem. Soc., 1951, 73, 502; id. ibid., 1952, 74, 4567; H. Burton and P. F. G. Praill, Quart. Revs. (London), 1952, 6, 302.
103. S. H. Bauer et al., J. Amer. Chem. Soc., 1943, 65, 889; id. ibid, 1945, 67, 339.
104. V. V. Chelintsev, Organic Catalysts, Izvest. Akad. Nauk SSSR, Moscow, 1939.
105. G. E. Coates and R. A. Whitcombe, J. Chem. Soc., 1956, 3351.
106. K. Watanabe and J. R. Motte, J. Chem. Phys., 1957, 26, 1773.
107. W. C. Price, Chem. Revs., 1947, 41, 257.
108. R. L. Amster and R. C. Taylor, Spectrochimica Acta, 1964, 20, 1487.
109. G. Oulevey and B. P. Susz, Helv. Chim. Acta, 1964, 47, 1828.

# CHAPTER 7

# APPLICATIONS OF MOLECULAR COMPLEXES

THE applications and uses of molecular or addition complexes range over a wide field, from medicine to chemistry in its widest aspects. Thus the greater part of the literature concerned with the acceptor boron trifluoride deals with the problem of catalysis.[1] This catalytic activity of boron trifluoride has attracted the attention of industrial chemists and research workers for nearly ninety years. It is claimed, for instance, that two Russians, V. Goryanov and A. M. Butlerov, achieved the polymerization of isobutylene to di-isobutylene in 1873 by using boron trifluoride as a catalyst.[2] The 1930's saw a marked resurgence of interest in this field because of the marked ability of the trifluoride to form complexes, which play an important part in acid catalysis in reactions involving polymerization, alkylation, condensation, isomerization, degradation and numerous other chemical syntheses. The catalytic activity of boron trifluoride is superior in many reactions to that of mineral acids or halogen compounds of metals, particularly since it is frequently unaccompanied by undesirable side-reactions. On the other hand, the complexes of boron trifluoride display an astonishing versatility, their use depending on the type of the reaction studied. Their mode of action is based, in general, on the increase of valency of the acceptor and donor atoms during complex formation; this leads to a weakening of the intramolecular bonds and to an increase in interatomic distances in the molecule of the complex. As a result, the donor moieties are activated and easily enter into different reactions with the substrate. An extensive review of the catalytic applications of boron trifluoride and its molecular complexes is given by Topchiev et al.[2]

There is also another point to be considered in connection with the general problem of catalysis. This concerns substrates made up of molecules with polar multiple bonds, which participate in reactions catalysed by electron donors or acceptors.[3] In these reactions an equilibrium is established between the reactants, catalysts and complexes formed; the existence of the latter is confirmed by the appearance of new infrared absorption bands and the shift of the ultraviolet bands of the reactants. For example,[2] during the interaction of phenyl-isocyanate with an excess of triethylamine in paraffin oil a new infrared band appears at 1635–1652 cm$^{-1}$, and the ultra-violet band of the cyanate is shifted from 41,000 to 37,000 cm$^{-1}$.

## *Adsorption*

The problem of catalysis is, of course, intimately connected with adsorption on surfaces. According to Mulliken,[4] the adsorption of certain molecules on metallic surfaces is accom-panied by a transfer of an electron from a donor atom to an acceptor atom with the resulting formation of a (charge-transfer) molecular complex. The bonding of this complex may range from strongly ionic to weakly covalent. In addition the repulsion between the quasi-ions in the adsorbate may be considered responsible for the observed decrease of the heat of adsorption with the increasing coverage of the catalytic surface. Also, since the energy level in the complex is lower than the Fermi level of the catalytic metal, the adsorption process involving electron transfer from the adsorbate to the metal may well be exothermic, though the ionization potential of the donor is generally larger than the work function of the acceptor surface of the metal. Theoretical calculations of the heats of adsorption at zero coverage lead to values in good agreement with experi-ment.[5] Furthermore, the charge-transfer theory of molecular complex formation leads to finite surface potentials,[6] and it is capable of predicting their signs: positive, if the adsorbate is a

Lewis base, i.e. an electron acceptor species; negative, if the adsorbate functions as a Lewis acid, i.e. an electron donor species.[7] In general, the adsorbate functions as a donor, so that the sign of the surface potentials is usually positive.[8] Thus the adsorption of inert (donor) gases on a nickel acceptor surface leads to a positive surface potential.[9]

This treatment has also been extended to adsorbents of the $p$-type semiconductors.[10] In this case the Fermi level increases greatly with increasing coverage of the surface,[11] leading to a limited coverage,[12] in agreement with experiment.[13]

A somewhat related topic is that of adsorption in dyeing.[14] Refractometric studies of the aqueous solutions of molecular complexes formed between aromatic compounds (dyes) and substances present in fibres, e.g. "nylon", "terylene", acrylonitrile or proteins, show that a hydrogen-bonded complex is formed between the dye and fibre, though the whole of the adsorbed dye may not be taken up by this mechanism.

The adsorption of molecular complexes or their components on surfaces could also find some use in the preparation of complexes by crystal growth at interfaces. For instance, the donor 1,4-diaminodurene will deposit from its very dilute solution ($6 \cdot 8 \times 10^{-5}$M) in petroleum ether on a single crystal of the acceptor $p$-chloranil, forming a $1:1$ complex.[15] The remainder of the amine will then deposit on the layer of the complex in a matter of hours, the growth of the crystals occurring in small concentrated zones near the least soluble component. This procedure may be used for the production of solid crystalline molecular complexes. Another method consists of preparing compact discs of each constituent (about $0 \cdot 5$ g) by compressing them in a 13 mm die at 3000 atm; these discs are then placed a few millimetres apart in a poor solvent. It is found that crystals will grow on the acceptor disc.

Another aspect of the use of molecular complexes in surface problems is lubrication. Some molecular complexes have found an important use as lubricants, displaying in some instances properties superior to those of the usual lubricating agents. For example, the iodine–$n$-butylbenzene complex is a very useful boundary lubricant of titanium.[16] Indeed, the usual lubricants have but a slight action on the metal.[17]

## Semiconductivity

An important application of molecular complex formation is in the realm of semiconductivity. For instance, the complexes formed by chloranil with $p$-phenylenediamine, diaminodurene, perylene or 3,10-diaminopyrene have been studied[18] with the emphasis on resistivities and Seebeck coefficients of the compressed microcrystalline material, and on the effect of temperature and unpaired electron-spin concentrations. These complexes display lower resistivities than the component organic moieties. Furthermore, the experimental results agree with those derived by measuring the semiconductor properties of single crystals of the complexes. Similar considerations apply to molecular complexes formed by perylene with iodine or 3,10-diaminopyrene, or by chloranil with 1,6-diaminopyrene. Chloranil also forms semiconducting complexes with dimethylaniline[19] and phthalocyanine.[20]

Certain proteins give rise through molecular complex formation to semiconductor substances.[21] Dry proteins show a very high resistivity and energy-gap, typical values of which are $10^{18}$ ohm cm and 2·8 eV, respectively.[22] The conductances may be considerably increased by complexing the protein with $p$-chloranil. For instance, a bovine plasma albumin–chloranil complex had in the dry state at room temperature a resistivity of only $3 \times 10^{12}$ ohm cm and an energy-gap of 1·06 eV; the relative values of a dry film of the albumin were $8 \times 10^{17}$ ohm cm and 2·80 eV, respectively. Hence, complex formation brought about an increase of the specific conductivity of the protein by a factor of $3 \times 10^5$. Moreover, the admission of water vapour into the vessel containing the complex at a vapour pressure chosen to give approximately a Brunauer–Emmett–Teller monolayer over the available surface of the substance gave a twelvefold increase in resistivity; this behaviour is quite different from that of uncomplexed bovine serum albumin. It is also worth noting that the complex showed a definite electron resonance signal, with a $g$-value of 1·998 and a line width of 6 gauss. There was no optical absorption or photoconductivity at a wavelength corresponding to the energy-gap of 1·06 eV.

Eley and co-workers[21] explained these results by postulating that the chloranil molecules accept electrons from the protein, thus creating positive holes in its conductivity band.[23] In accordance with this hypothesis, water will neutralize the positive holes by donating electrons and thus lower the conductivity of the complex. Ammonia gas was also found to exert a similar effect, since it is an electron donor. These studies have been extended to the bromanil and iodanil complexes of the protein with similar results.

Semiconductor properties are not, however, generally applicable to all molecular complexes. Thus the important class of aromatic hydrocarbon–amine complexes do not appear to display semiconductor properties.[24] A more detailed treatment of charge-transfer complexes and their use as semiconductors has been published recently.[25] The theoretical aspect of electron conduction in charge-transfer complexes has been treated by the L. C. A. O. method of molecular orbitals, combined with crystal-field splitting calculations,[26] in order to obtain values for the activation energy of electron conduction, the complex examined being triethylammonium-(tetracyanoquino dimethan)$_2$.

## Synthetic applications

Another important field of application is concerned with the synthesis of organic compounds. For example, the molecular complexes of alkali metal hydrides,[27] such as lithium tri-tert-butoxyaluminohydride LiAlH (OCMe$_3$)$_3$, can be reacted with various acyl chlorides in diglyme at $-78°$ C to yield the corresponding aldehydes.

Some of the molecular complexes formed by the synthetic procedures above can also be used as intermediates for further synthesis. Thus, if diketene is reacted with methyl-tert-butyl-carbodiimide[28] in an inert solvent in the presence of cuprous chloride as catalyst, a solid molecular complex is formed (m.p. 75°C), which is soluble in 2 N–HCl solution and is used as an intermediate in the synthesis of more complex materials. Another example is concerned with 1-methyl-pyridinium iodide; in this case a donor moiety adds at the 4-position,[29] and in aqueous solution of the iodide itself association of the compound results in charge-transfer complex formation.[30] Molecular complex formation also occurs during the nitration of aromatic com-pounds.[31] Solutions of most aromatic hydrocarbons in nitro-methane give coloured solutions in the presence of a little aluminium chloride, e.g. benzene gives a red solution, while naphthalene yields an orange solution; the electron acceptor in this case is the complex $AlCl_3$–$MeNO_2$, as shown by electron-spin resonance. For instance, a 2% solution of aluminium chloride in nitrobenzene reacts with the compound $[(p\text{-}MeOC_6H_4)_2\text{-}C:]_2$ to give a univalent positive ion with strong electron-spin reson-ance. Similarly, the characteristic colour of the solutions of substituted benzenes in the presence of nitric acid in nitro-methane and the correlation between colour and nitration velocity indicates charge-transfer complex formation as a step in the process. The study of the mechanism of chemical reactions has also been extended to the inorganic field. For example, the reduction of bromate by chloride involves the transient forma-tion of a molecular complex and not of a radical.[32]

The relation between molecular complex formation and the mechanism of aromatic substitution has been studied by Brown,[33] who proposed a mechanism for aromatic (Ar) and electrophilic (E) substitution involving the successive formation of inter-molecular charge-transfer complexes, viz.

$$E \ldots Ar^+ - H \quad \text{and} \quad H \ldots Ar^+ - E$$

followed by the base-catalysed loss of protons. This concept enables one to predict the orientations and the relative reactivities of positions in aromatic compounds towards electrophilic sub-stitution. Molecular orbital calculations lead to factors known as $Z$-values, which are indices of chemical reactivities. Better results are claimed by this method than by the use of concepts of atom-localization energies[34] or superdelocalizability.[35] This theory also gives a quantum-mechanical basis for the selectivity relation of Brown and Nelson.[36]

## Analytical applications

The concept of molecular complexes is also of importance in analytical chemistry. For instance, molecular complex formation has been used in identifying compounds by means of spot tests.[37]

Another example concerns the identification of alkyl-benzyl sulphides by reacting the latter with mercuric chloride in water or ethanol solution to form molecular complexes.[38] Isomers can be separated by means of complex formation, e.g. the γ- and δ-isomers of hexachlorocyclohexane[39] are separated by reacting the mixture with anthranilic acid; the γ-isomer forms a 1:2 complex with the acid (m.p. 127°C) and can thus be separated from the δ-compound. Gases can be separated by forming suitable molecular complexes and subjecting them to chromatography. For example, columns of ferrous sulphate on a suitable support give a good separation of nitric oxide from other gases.[40] The boron trifluoride–methanol complex may be used for the routine analysis of fatty acids by gas chromatography;[41] the complex is also used catalytically for determining alcoholic hydroxyl groups and aliphatic caboxylic acids. The identification of certain organic compounds is facilitated by the spectrophotometric determination of their molecular weights via the complexes formed with picrates.[42]

## Applications in biology

Molecular complex formation has found some uses in biology.[4,29,43] Thus the addition of di- or tri-phosphopyridine nucleotide to indole derivatives produces a yellow solution and a new diffuse band appears on the long wavelength side of the indole absorption spectrum; electron transfer occurs from the indole nucleus to the pyrimidine co-enzyme.[44]

It is worth noting that nucleic acid bases form molecular complexes with chloranil.[45] These complexes may be prepared by dissolving the bases, adenine, cytosine, thymine or guanine in dimethylsulphoxide in the presence of chloranil; a 1 : 1 complex is then produced, which has a stability constant of $10^{-2}$, as calculated by the Benesi–Hildebrand equation. This procedure was developed on the basis of the Szent-Györgyi's postulate[46,47] that molecular (charge-transfer) complexes may play a fundamental part in biological processes.

The electron donor and acceptor properties of some hormones have also been investigated and their capacities determined in respect to charge-transfer[46,48] by spectrophotometry of charge-transfer bands and polarography in organic solvents. Tryptamine, prolactin, oestrone and some synthetic oestrogens were found to be good electron donors, while most steroids acted as electron acceptors. It has been suggested by Allison[48] that hydrogen bonding and charge-transfer complex formation may play an important part in hormonal action. Indeed, the causative relation between molecular complex formation and drug action has also come under scrutiny. For instance, reserpine and the phenothiazine tranquilizers[43] (Lyons and Mackie) have electron-donating properties. In line with the hypothesis concerning the relation between drug activity and charge transfer,[49] it was suggested that[50] specific drug activity can result when a strong electron donor or acceptor molecule contains a side-chain capable of hydrogen bonding, e.g. chlorpromazine.

Chlorpromazine has received a great deal of attention in connection with complex formation. For instance, it forms a charge transfer complex with flavin mononucleotide and serotonin.[46] It also forms a complex with rhodamine B[56] and with xanthene dyes.[57] In the latter case the peak of the absorption spectrum is shifted to longer wavelengths by about 35 m$\mu$. It is postulated that the formation of the complexes by chlorpromazine may cause the observed inhibition of photon-induced muscular contraction, which is photo-sensitized by xanthene dyes.

An interesting reaction between a drug and a nucleic acid is that between procaine (p-aminobenzoyl-diethylaminoethanol) and RNA or its hydrochloric acid hydrolysates.[51] An intense magenta colour develops during the reaction with an absorption peak at 550 m$\mu$; the colour is stable for several months at 0°C. The reaction is due to the ribose moiety, since procaine does not react with nucleic acid bases or phosphoric acid; there is also no reaction between procaine and DNA. The interaction between RNA and procaine is of the charge-transfer $\pi$-type, since a new intense band is formed at longer wavelengths than those of the constitutents; this new band has also a negative temperature coefficient. It is possible that molecular complex formation is related to the anaesthetic action of the drug.

The possible correlation between the electron donor or electron-acceptor capacities of aromatic molecules, as determined by the ionization or reduction potentials, and their carcinogenic activity was examined for the first time by the Pullman brothers[52] in 1950; this idea was then developed by others as well.[47] A very recent paper by Allison and Nash[48] advances the proposition that "carcinogeneity arises as a result of a suitable combination of both electron-donor and electron-acceptor properties of a compound". This hypothesis has been attacked by the Pullmans,[47,53] who advocate instead a theory based on the reactivities of the K and L regions in aromatic hydrocarbons. Furthermore, Epstein[54] and others[55] found no particular association between the formation of molecular complexes and carcinogenesis in the case of 107 polycyclic hydrocarbon compounds. Experimental evidence does not support the suggestion that charge-transfer tests can be used to screen for carcinogeneity.[54] It is considered unlikely that charge-transfer complex formation plays a significant part in determining the carcinogeneity of polycyclic compounds of the aromatic type.

## References

1. D. KÄSTNER, Newer Methods of Preparative Organic Chemistry, Interscience Publ., New York, 1958.
2. A. V. TOPCHIEV et al., Boron Fluoride and its Compounds as Catalysts in Organic Chemistry, Pergamon Press, London, 1959, p. 10; H. S. BOOTH and D. R. MARTIN, J. Amer. Chem. Soc., 142, 64, 2198.
3. M. PESTEMER and D. LAUERER, Z. Angew. Chem., 1960, 72, 612.
4. R. S. MULLIKEN, J. Amer. Chem. Soc., 1952, 74, 811.
5. J. C. MIGNOLET, Bull. Soc. Chim. Belges, 1955, 64, 126; R. J. BRODD, J. Phys. Chem., 1958, 62, 54.
6. W. M. H. SACHTLER, Ph. D. Diss., Braunschweig, Germany, 1952.
7. J. J. BROEDER et al., Z. Elektrochem., 1956, 60, 838.
8. S. P. McGLYNN, Chem. Revs., 1958, 58, 1113.
9. A. A. FROST, Trans. Electrochem. Soc., 1942, 82, 259; J. C. P. MIGNOLET, Disc. Faraday Soc., 1950, 8, 105.
10. F. A. MATSEN et al., J. Chem. Phys., 1954, 22, 1800.
11. P. B. WEISZ, J. Chem. Phys., 1953, 21, 2236.
12. M. BOUDART, J. Amer. Chem. Soc., 1952, 74, 1531.
13. E. L. COOK and N. HACKERMAN, J. Phys. and Coll. Chem., 1951, 55, 549; N. HACKERMAN and A. H. ROEBUCK, Ind. Eng. Chem., 1954, 46, 1481.
14. D. S. E. CAMPBELL et al., J. Soc. Dyers and Colour, 1957, 73, 546.
15. P. L. KRONICK and M. M. LABES, J. Chem. Phys., 1961, 35, 2011; M. M. LABES and H. UR, Org. Chem., 1961, 26, 4760; H. SCOTT et al., Nature, (London), 1963, 197, 375.
16. R. W. ROBERTS and R. S. OWENS, Nature, (London), 1963, 200, 357.
17. R. V. KLINT and R. S. OWENS, A.S.L.E.Trans., 1962, 5, 105.

18. M. M. Labes *et al.; Proc. Intern. Conf. Semiconductor Phys. Prague*, 1960, 850; M. M. Labes, *J. Chem. Phys.*, 1961, **35**, 2016.
19. D. D. Eley *et al., Trans. Faraday Soc.*, 1959, **28**, 54.
20. G. Tollin *et al., J. Chem. Phys.*, 1960, **32**, 1020.
21. D. D. Eley *et al., Nature (London)*, 1960, **188**, 724.
22. M. H. Cardew and D. D. Eley, *Trans. Faraday Soc.*, 1959, **27**, 115.
23. M. G. Evans and J. Gergely, *J. Biochim. Biophys. Acta*, 1949, **3**, 188.
24. H. Kuroda *et al., Bull. Chem. Soc. Japan*, 1962, **35**, 1604.
25. *Organic Semiconductors, Procs. Conf.*, editor Brophy, Macmillan, London, 1963.
26. E. Menefee and Yoh-Ham-Pao, *J. Chem. Phys.*, 1962, **36**, 3472.
27. H. C. Brown and B. C. Subha Rao, *J. Amer. Chem. Soc.*, 1958, **80**, 5377.
28. R. Hofmann *et al.*, German Patent 960,458, 1957; 960,458.
29. E. M. Kosower, *J. Amer. Chem. Soc.*, 1956, **78**, 3493.
30. E. M. Kosower and J. C. Burbach, *J. Amer. Chem. Soc.*, 1956, **78**, 5838.
31. H. M. Buck *et al., Tetrahedron Letters*, 1960, No. 9, 5.
32. J. Sigalla, *J. Chim. Phys.*, 1958, **55**, 758.
33. R. D. Brown, *J. Chem. Soc.*, 1959, 2232, 2234.
34. M. J. S. Dewar and E. W. T. Warford, *J. Chem. Soc.*, 1956, 3581.
35. K. Fukui *et al., J. Chem. Phys.*, 1957, **27**, 1247.
36. L. N. Ferguson and A. Y. Garner, *J. Amer. Chem. Soc.*, 1954, **76**, 1167.
37. F. Feigl, *Spot Tests in Organic Chemistry*, 5th ed., Elsevier, New York, 1958, p. 327.
38. M. Večeřa *et al., Chem. Listy*, 1958, **52**, 144; id., *Collection Czekoslovak. Chem. Communs.*, 1959, **24**, 640.
39. H. Furst and K. Praeger, *Chem. Tech. Berlin*, 1958, **10**, 603.
40. U. Schwenk and M. Hachenberger, *Brennstoff Chem.*, 1960, **41**, 183.
41. J. Mitchell, jnr. *et al., J. Amer. Chem. Soc.*, 1940, **62**, 4; L. D. Metcalfe and A. A. Schmitz, *Anal. Chem.*, 1961, **33**, 363.
42. K. J. Cunningham *et al., J. Chem. Soc.*, 1951, 2305; Yu. N. Sheinker and B. M. Golovner, *Izvest. Akad. Nauk SSSR, Ser. Fiz.*, 1953, **17**, 681; V. I. Siele and J. B. Picard, *Appl. Spectroscopy*, 1958, **12**, 8.
43. R. Beukers and A. Szent-Györgyi, *Rec. Trav. Chim.*, 1962, **81**, 255; L. E. Lyons and J. C. Mackie, *Nature (London)*, 1963, **197**, 589.
44. G. Cilento and P. Guisti, *J. Amer. Chem. Soc.*, 1959, 81, 3801.
45. P. Machmer and J. Duchesne, *Nature (London)*, 1965, **206**, 618.
46. A. Szent-Györgyi, *Introduction to Submolecular Biology*, Acad. Press, New York, 1960.
47. A. Szent-Györgyi *et al., Proc. U.S. Natl. Akad. Sci.*, 1960, **46**, 1444; R. Mason, *Nature (London)*, 1958, **181**, 820; J. E. Lovelock *et al.*, ibid., 1962, **193**, 540; T. M. Wong *et al., Cancer Research*, 1962, **22**, 1053; A. Pullman and B. Pullman, *Nature (London)*, 1962, **196**, 228.
48. A. C. Allison and T. Nash, *Nature (London)*, 1963, **197**, 758; V. Westphal and B. D. Ashley, *J. Biol. Chem.*, 1962, **237**, 2763; A. C. Allison *et al., Life Sciences*, 1962, No. 12, 729–37, Pergamon Press, U.S.A.
49. G. Karreman *et al., Science*, 1959, **130**, 1191.
50. T. Nash and A. C. Allison, *Biochem. Pharmacology*, Pergamon Press, Oxford, 1963.
51. D. Agin, *Nature (London)*, 1965, **205**, 805.
52. A. Pullman and B. Pullman, *Cancérisation par les Substances Chimiques et Structure Moléculaire*, Mason, Paris, 1955.

53. A. PULLMAN and B. PULLMAN, *Nature (London)*, 1963, **199**, 467; id., *Advances in Cancer Research*, 1955,**3**, 117.
54. S. E. EPSTEIN *et al.*, *Nature (London)*, 1964, **204**, 750; S. E. EPSTEIN *et al.*, *Cancer Research*, 1964,**24**, 855.
55. N. P. BUU-HOI and P. JACQUIGNON, *Experientia*, 1957, **13**, 375.
56. P. S. GUTH and M. A. SPIRTES, *Intern. Rev. Neurobiol.*, 1964, **7**, 231; A. SZENT-GYÖRGYI, *Bioenergetics*, Acad. Press, New York, 1957.
57. E. LÁBOS, *Nature (London)*, 1966,**209**, 201.

# INDEX

(Names of authors mentioned in the text but not in the references are given here;
figures in **bold** type refer to more detailed treatment)

171